BUILD

UNIVERSES

Ron Connors

Failed Artist:
A potpourri of tales from the
trenches… of life

© 2024 **Europe Books** | London
www.europebooks.co.uk | info@europebooks.co.uk

ISBN 9791220147545
First edition: February 2024

Failed Artist:
A potpourri of tales from the trenches... of life

To Phuong Mai, Nambo, Pascal and Gary.

Thanks for the love. support, and inspiration.

"I have two words for every person in the world. For those who love and support me, those words are "Thank You!" For the rest, one of those words is "you" but the other one ain't "thank.".

Table of Contents

Introduction

A man can fall down many, many times, but he's never a failure until he refuses to get back up.

Evel Knievel

Failure (N.) One who fears success. A person with the ability to snatch defeat from the jaws of certain victory. An individual with the ability to lose at all costs.

Author's definition

I remember one fellow who loves being called an "artist" telling me that he would never hang his work in a cafe or restaurant.

"I did that when I was in college... high school," he said.

I am sure that he noted my snicker as he knew that I have quite a few pieces hanging in places like the JW Marriott in Ha Noi and some of the trendier restaurants here.

"I certainly wouldn't want them languishing in some hotel," he spouted. It sounded to me as though we were playing chess, and he was declaring checkmate.

"How do you go about selling your work?" I asked.

"Artists don't sell their work. Their work sells them," He replied.

I thought this a bit peculiar as this fellow has a habit of asking people to take photos of him posing in front of art pieces and such, art pieces that are not his creations. He could be best described as an "attention whore". He is also rather well established as a mooch. I chuckle as I recalled him telling me he would never be so vain as to

13

name a gallery after himself, as I did mine. Yet when a girl he was dating opened a small boutique and gave him a tiny space on her second floor, he pasted a large decal, with his name, on the largest bit of window on the front of the space.

It is all rather comical.

Destiny is a feeling that you know something about yourself that nobody else does. The picture that you have in your own mind of what you are about will come true.

Bob Dylan

Failing as an artist is achievement. I have learned this from many. I have been told again and again that artists don't care about money. They don't care about sales. They only care about art... It is intriguing yet fills me with dismay. I am nearly always overjoyed when something I create sells. When someone visits my place or comes by my stall at a market, I often feel so desperate for a sale that I want to beg! It would be an exaggeration to say that I cannot count the number of times when someone has shown what seems like genuine interest in a piece of my work and I have literally talked them out of buying it but... I can genuinely state that the times that this has occurred far outnumber the times when I have allowed a purchase! Oh, my goodness! Does this mean I am a true artist?

I suppose self-sabotage is as much a part the character make-up of the failed artist as his inability to bend to the rules of convention. While many in the art world seem to follow a sort of template, a failed artist "goes his own way", stubbornly refusing to comply with that which would have him recognized as an artist. The flashy scarves and tilted berets that are the signature wear in the art world are notably lacking in his wardrobe. Goatees and tattoos are absent as well. In his art, the recognizable traces of Picasso, Klimt, Van Gogh, Basquiat are not there. Perhaps out of ignorance of what makes an artist great or simply the inability to navigate in his own world, like the proverbial sailor cursed with cloudy skies. The impenetrable fog in which he walks leaves him blind to all but what he alone can see. And the limits of his vision are infinite, infinite in their finiteness.

The confidence to know when to quit

The problem of having a conscience in a world of the unconscious is that one consciously pays debts that are not owed while unconsciously acquiring debts that don't exist. This is commonly known as overthinking. In reality any thinking is overthinking. In other words, it is not normal, perhaps a subject for study.

An example: When a person of conscience sees an advertisement about children who are without regular meals, he/she feels obliged, not necessarily to act but rather to feel. And that feeling leads the person to act, not necessarily to reply to the appeal for funds but rather to conduct oneself in a way that deprives him/her of the joy that one without conscience feels while experiencing activities which the "normal" soul relishes as he/she parties away. While the person of conscience believes him/herself to be practicing humility he/she is really being condescending to a point of absolute ridiculousness. She/he is displaying an air of superiority, an exaggerated sense of self-importance, a kind of super-hero complex.

The desire to show empathy for those in need is the desire to find those who need assistance even if that assistance is only the need to have someone care about another's situation. Folks without conscience are willing to express outrage at the criticism of the rich and famous, claiming that they deserve what they have and anyone who does not agree is merely jealous and envious. Those with conscience can understand this and perhaps even empathize while contending that there are folks more deserving of empathy. They claim a rage against a world or system which not only creates inequality but promotes it. While this may seem commendable it normally only promotes further inequality as it feeds into an "us against them" scenario despite intentions of bringing people together. This is sometimes conscious, as folks, probably more often than not, don't truly care about the target of their concern but rather that others recognize that they are genuine, caring people who devote their lives to helping others and they expect to be recognized for this.

Recognizing that I may only know this to be true of me, I experience regular evidence of this virtually anytime I associate with people. This is probably why I feel a bit of greatness whenever I am creating something yet don't feel any sort of satisfaction when someone relates to me that something that I have created is great. This is not to say that I can't appreciate a compliment or be desirous of an affirmation of my work but rather that I could not care less about the opinions of others and certainly do not seek or appreciate constructive criticism.

Even the least critical reader could note that this is a recipe for failure. While a person may applaud me for this attitude, the same person's applause can be given generously with the certainty that nothing I create will cost them a penny out of their pocket or crowd a step on their own ladder to success even if they have no intention of moving up. My lack of desire to please others ensures my failure and failure becomes the objective of my creation! (A round of applause please!)

Two Wheels

I was on a road trip. I had left Torreon, Mexico and was heading towards Montana. I didn't need to be back in Torreon for a couple of months, so I had no real need to rush but I do like to rush when I am on a motorcycle. I find it hard to stay in one place for more than a few days and often find myself bored anytime I am not on the bike. And... when I am on the bike, I often catch myself day-dreaming when I am not speeding or putting my riding skills to a test while flying through some curves. Jamming through some sort of weather that leaves most other bikers seeking shelter is another favourite. This should come as no surprise as most who ride find pleasure in risk and those that don't brag that they do.

This is not so different than art. Most artists lay claim to some sort of individuality, originality, and creativity, which sets them apart from all others. This would make risk inherent in their art as those who live by the sword must die by the sword and the further away one is from a commercial audience, the closer one is to starvation.

The heat of the sun was so intense that the asphalt was melting, and the road was actually a bit slick. Traffic on the motorway was so impacted that even splitting lanes wasn't getting me much in the way of forward progress. The heat emanating from the vehicles was augmenting that from the sun and I eventually found myself in a town just off the main road. This was frightening because I had no conscious memory of leaving the motorway and I realized that I had most likely blacked out for a bit at some point. Anyone who has ever experienced heat stroke can understand this. One goes in and out of consciousness while remaining upright as the muscles still receive signals though mindfulness is absent, and one is essentially on autopilot.

I saw a policeman directing traffic and pulled over to get directions back to the motorway. This only added to my confusion when I saw his vehicle parked just off the road. It was an old VW Bug decked out in its official police regalia and it seemed such an anachronism that I suppose I wondered if I had wandered into some sort of time warp. I got an adrenaline rush from this fear and spun the rear tire on the oily pavement as I took off, something of which I did not suspect my mellow Moto Guzzi to be capable. This woke me up, which was most likely the Guzzi's intention, and my relief at being back on the motorway was an additional boost. I began calculating my arrival at the Mexico-Texas border in hopes of hitting it before or after the busiest of times, between 4 p.m. and 6 p.m.

I was past most of the industrial zones north of Torreon and I had managed to get on to a two-lane road that had very little in the way of traffic and I started to make good time. I am a sucker for nostalgia though, and as I was approaching a small oasis town, I saw a cantina that looked straight out of a movie of the Old West. I slowed and when I read the sign that announced that they served *carne de chivo*, goat meat, they had me.

I parked my beautiful two tone blue Guzzi in front of the largest window in the place and sat down at table where I could clearly witness its theft were that to occur. I supposed that intervening in its theft was probably not advisable in the land of the *sicario*, but I thought it would not be unreasonable to ask for the bag on back with my belongings before they took possession of the bike.

20

Bob Seger wrote a song called "Turn the Page". It often goes through my head when I am travelling on two wheels. There is something about motorcycling that brings out the worst in people. Strangers who would normally ignore you and not care whether you are alive or dead suddenly seem to wish you were the latter.

"Well you walk into a restaurant
Strung out from the road
And you feel the eyes upon you
As you're shakin' off the cold
You pretend it doesn't bother you
But you just want to explode

Most times you can't hear 'em talk
Other times you can
All the same old cliches
"Is that a woman or a man?"
And you always seem outnumbered
You don't dare make a stand."

The view from the window seat was magnificent as I looked out onto the desert. The heat waves lazily obscured the view of some palm trees in the distance. The restaurant was amazingly clean and obviously the hangout for wealthy locals who I suppose seemed stereotypical to me in their cowboy regalia. Cowboy hats that are too new or too clean shout "*narco*" to me; whether that is fair or not cannot be for me to decide, only to beware.

There were a few flies present and they paid much more attention to me than did the waiter. When I did manage to get the waiter to bring a menu, he assured me that anything on the special board was sold out and even items on the menu were unavailable. I ordered a beer and assured him that I would not be leaving until I was served the house special. I added that the chef needn't bother urinating on the food as I wasn't worth his piss and the waiter chuckled, left, and returned instantly with a bucket of ice-cold beer and a much warmer demeanour. He proceeded to make his rounds obviously sharing the crazy gringo's joke. Being a good sport is always better than being an arrogant fool, which is a Mexican stereotype of gringo tourists, and I recognized that I had burned that particular bridge and built another one as several of them turned towards me and gave me a good-natured tilt of a beer bottle, tip of the hat or nod of the head. I was no longer concerned for my bike or my own welfare. Call it unfair to the rest of the inhabitants on the planet but I trust Mexicans like no others.

There was no way that I was leaving without finishing that bucket and I knew that a shot or two of something would be showing up at some point, so I resigned myself to a night's stay in what I was told was the town's only hotel. This is usually fine, but it can be a bit awkward as small-town hotels often double as brothels. I don't mind the concept but the sound of the headboard in the next room slamming against the adjoining wall can be a bit unsettling. My fame passed its fifteen-minute mark and the waiter's story had apparently become stale as the rest of the folks returned their focus to their own business. I was left alone to finish an exquisite meal of fresh corn tortillas, tender roasted goat, wonderfully cooked beans, and rice that was stuff of the gods.

Thankfully the shots never came and my enthusiasm for the icy beer waned as I toyed with the idea of continuing on to the border. My confidence was high, and I felt completely refreshed, so refreshed that the thought of doing anything besides crushing a few more beers and maybe taking a walk around the town seemed unappealing despite the temptation to make up some time. Having made what I figured was a good decision and having been assured that the hotel really was about a kilometre away I ordered a shot of tequila and felt free. There is no failure in knowing when to quit. Whether one wants to admit it or not, every day is a journey. Time is what one makes of it and there is little in life that a decision won't change. When one decides to be happy, happiness comes. Want some misery? Just decide to be miserable.

My decision to take it easy came with a surprise. As I had been nearly unconscious in the heat, it had not occurred to me that it was barely past noon. My early start had been a good idea, but like many good ideas it had been shared by the masses and the congestion on the main road slowed us all down to a crawl. As I looked up at the sun in the centre of the sky, I realised that the next day's ride was going to be a long one as I would be making up for the time I was borrowing on this day. But I figured that a four-a.m. departure from this little place in Chihuahua would put me at the border about ten or eleven and with any luck traffic would be light by then. Once in the states, it would be just a question of pegging it and avoiding speed traps. I have done many a mile in several states and have rarely been pulled over. Even when I have been stopped, I have always got off with a warning.

The hotel was clean, comfortable, and cheap. It was a lot less dodgy than I had imagined; it had a gated parking area with 24-hour security, so it seemed like a winner. I felt like taking a nap, but I thought it best to go exploring to work off some of the early buzz. In my dehydrated state the little bit of alcohol that I consumed had gone straight to my head.

The cobblestone streets had a fine layer of dust on them, which would rise with the soft breeze that would blow from time to time. The dust came from the sidewalks, which were almost dust free. It reminded me of the daily regimens of the ladies in Colonia Linda Vista back when I lived in Guadalajara. They would be out with their brooms two or three times a day dusting off the sidewalks and giving stern looks to anyone who had the gall to use them. The sidewalks were an extension of the homes that lined them, much like a front porch.

Between twelve and two, most folks have the good sense to take a siesta, not just in Mexico but in many places. Call it laziness but folks who are too uptight to recognize the benefits of this mid-day relaxation are most likely more stressed than they need be. I find it pleasant to walk at such times as I can almost feel the peace of those who are sleeping.

My Tony Lamas are almost as comfortable as sneakers, but I did feel I was making an excess of noise and wished I had changed them for sneakers before I left the hotel. I made it to the plaza, a typically Mexican square with comfortable benches and nice shade trees. There was a statue in the middle. It was a black iron sculpture of some revolutionary figure or maybe an intellectual. It seemed like a fine place to smoke but I don't like to smoke without a drink, so I abstained. I made a tiny sketch of the park in my pocketbook with a ball-point pen. I saw a temporarily abandoned *puesto* with Carne Asada painted prominently on it and decided that tacos would definitely be on the menu that evening. I headed back the room feeling quite content. I was happy that I left my camera in my bag. More often than not, I take photos as an obligation, something to show someone else.

At 3:30 a.m., I woke with the taste of tacos *el carbon* resting on my tongue. The toothbrush and toothpaste I found in the bathroom did little more than satisfy a habit. Brushing with them did not alter the residue of the smoky flavour I had in my mouth. It reminded me that I hadn't drunk any alcohol with the tacos, and I felt really ready to roll.

And roll I did. I ended up parking my bike and myself in a small town just outside of El Paso after a pretty decent ten hours. I had planned to go further but I wanted to watch a UFC event. And, as luck would have it, the fabulous sports bar there was having a rock and roll night, so it was all for naught. But I enjoyed a few of their songs and had a great burger. Hard to get bad food in Texas.

The Right to Fail

For all these failures, I have earned the right to fail.

Daniel Cormier

As I reflect upon the many people I can name who have had tremendous success on a superficial level, I am sometimes perplexed. When I write superficial level, I mean that people like me only know these successful folks for their successes and do not acknowledge their failures. When I look at some examples of them in the history of the art and music world: Janis Joplin, Jimmy Hendrix, John Belushi, Jean-Michel Basquiat, Jackson Pollock, and Vincent Van Gogh, I see in them tremendous success. In their lives, I note a frustration of failure. Were they failures in that which made them famous, they could have most likely lived longer and happier lives muddled in mediocrity rather than the meteoric flights to fame that seemed to set them aflame, and their lives roared like funeral pyres. But if it was so easy to fail, everyone would do it.

When I think about what most folks consider the lowest points of their lives, I wonder what they think about. For most people it must be something to do with drugs, and I include alcohol of course. When one states that he or she has hit rock bottom that usually means they have done something disgusting to embarrass themselves. It also includes something to do with substance abuse and finances. And then I meet someone who seems to have an idyllic lifestyle and they say that their favourite thing to do is to drink and take other drugs. Are they living on the rock bottom? Are they seeking it? Are they being saved

27

from hitting it by a significant other or the fact that they don't have the means and maybe even the courage to hit it? I have met one person, whose absolute favourite thing is to work. And when I say favourite thing, I mean Pierre is happiest when he is working. He would rather work than travel or party or anything else! I admire him, recognizing that in him I see what I most like about me. I understand him and when I leave dinners or parties or other social gatherings to go home and paint or play around creating something which ultimately has little or no value to anyone but myself, it is only to feed the part of me that loves my work. Whenever I hear of how amazing an event got after I left, I want to take responsibility for the success of the event. After all, wasn't it me who left? And did not my departure brighten things up?

I am often at my worst in conversations about art. I could not care less about waxing artsy or identifying all of the artists I can recognize by colour or brush stroke. I recall being asked a question at a very formal dinner I was invited to attend by a fellow who supports my art. He pointed at a piece of artwork that was hanging on the wall, an obvious Gustav Klimt copy. It is the type of thing I have seen entirely too much of in my life. He said, "What do you think of that painting?" I replied, as eloquently as I could muster at that moment, "I think it is horrible!" This perked up those around us. Prior to that, they had been stuck in the boredom of their focus on the subtle but unidentifiable flavours of a sautéed gnocchi dish they were busy dissecting and washing down with a Grand Cru. The excitement died immediately however as I failed to follow the comment with an explanation and perhaps a quick lesson in the finer things of the visual art world that I have often heard artsy folks provide. My friend smiled, and said, "I am glad you said that. I think it's horrible." And the waiting began yet again though most returned to their dissection.

I have said that "Frankness buys freedom.", though the frank are seldom free. Privileged folks often pretend they are being frank when they are being mean, and a "frank" opinion is usually just condescension wearing a poor disguise. But I am not one of the privileged but rather one with close to nothing and as has been said very well, perhaps best by Janis Joplin, when one has nothin', they have nothin' left to lose. And frank I remain while those with somethin' remain prisoners to something they call culture though they wish it was class.

I am sure there are many obsessed folks like Pierre, but he is the only one I know personally. But then, there are people who dedicate their lives to a profession that they hate. There are people who continue to work beyond retirement age despite an economic situation which would allow them a very healthy lifestyle. Some do it because they truly love what they do while others do it because they prefer existence to life. Their very lives depend upon what they believe is responsible for their existence. They may spout clichés like "Nothing is free." "Money doesn't solve everything." "There is no such thing as a free lunch." all the while financing lives for their children, which essentially ensure that those children, who are either adults or nearly that, will never have to struggle for anything despite their claims to do so. They insist on envy, disowning those who are not envious, claiming they are jealous, too bothered by their jealousy to envy them. Their only true companions are their work and the material wealth that comes from it and those who choose not to perform the slavish tasks which brought them to their "freedom" are lazy and impure. They are the bane

29

of society and should be reminded constantly that failure is not only their fate but is in their genes and their lack of discipline has been inherited from their parents and will condemn their children to a life of unnecessary struggle.

Perhaps one of the things that truly separates the superficially successful from the failures, is that the successful are always willing to believe in their own success. As an extension, they are always comfortable with their own work even when it is not done at a very high standard. This is not to say that successful people don't have high standards, it is merely to note that successful people understand that failure is part of a process and dwelling on minor hiccups is what keeps the failures failing.

Being an artist at failure, I understand that, to paraphrase Chael Sonnen, failure is always an option and sometimes it seems to be my only choice. Believing that a piece of my work is one of the greatest masterpieces of all time makes me want to quit more than anything I can imagine as failure. It makes me fear the fame and commercial success that would incline me to attempt to reproduce the "success" rather than create art regardless of remaining a "failure."

It is sad sometimes when I should be getting excited for an exhibition, and I find myself being not only stressed but in distress. Rather than taking care of last-minute details I am completely willing to leave, what I consider, well enough alone. I am even more desirous to just leave the exhibition, but this is hardly an option. I am sure a reader has a great quick solution, hire someone to take care of the details, but anyone with experience, who does not consider him or herself a perfectionist can relate. Hiring someone is a bit like assigning homework. Even the most dedicated students have questions, and one often

30

finds that a person best suited for a job has the most difficulty completing it.

It is easy for the "perfectionist" to get employees to do everything right as a perfectionist considers whatever they do as perfect, so the employee only needs to satiate the often sadistic and unreasonable desires of a perfect boss, which means make the boss feel like a boss. This is usually easier than it might seem. It is only the barking and the pettiness that are bothersome. When one has an employer who insists on workers who set their own standards, even the little bit of independence that the slave to perfection can muster dissipates as independence breeds responsibility just as collaboration demands attention. When one has the independent minded working on a collaboration, it is uncommonly essential for the person who is in charge to micromanage to ensure the project becomes a whole rather than a sum of its parts; this is where the stress comes in.

At my exhibitions, I am usually two or three cigarettes and four or five drinks in moments after the scheduled opening of a show and by the time the buyers and curators appear, I am well past tipsy and in need of a wall, well anchored table, or a generous soul to keep me upright. Visitors who insist on a tour seem more like officers administering a field test for drunken driving than people with an appreciation for art. But I have the right to decline, and I often do so. I am then at the mercy of an agent, usually an attractive young lady, who takes it upon herself to entertain the more attractive males in the crowd, usually one at a time. This leaves those truly interested in a purchase to their own devices and the art, which is subject to a purchase of impulse, remains safely on display unfettered by those nasty "sold" signs that steal so much of its dignity!

Patterns

If you are not moving forward, you are in your own way.

Ron Connors

When I was about 19 years old, I was forced to recognize a pattern. I did not know it at the time, but I was following a pattern that I had set for myself or maybe had been set for me much earlier than that. I worked as a bellman at a Sheraton Inn in Great Falls, Montana. There was nothing very remarkable about the job. It paid pretty well but the pay was minimum wage with tips and the "pretty well" came mostly from bus tours where the bellman on duty would make some pretty good bucks. We were paid a dollar per bag or something like that and, as there were usually at least fifty bags on a bus, the cumulative amount was an enormous sum at that time. I remember on days when there was a tour, the desk staff, especially the front desk manager, would treat me like a moron, even sometimes rushing out from behind the desks to steal a few bags and a few bucks. I found it incredible that adults would exhibit this type of behaviour, but it was the norm. In addition to this income, we would periodically be called upon to deliver a room service, another thing that one of the co-workers/competitors would weasel in on at times. A tip was added to the bill and customers would almost always hand one a dollar or two in addition to this. There were also services that an enterprising bellman could provide from scoring a bag of marijuana to driving a customer to one of the local restaurants or bars as the taxi service in town was lacking. But at the end of the day, a bellman's final income was pretty much determined by luck and that was fine with me and the rest of the crew.

One day the world there was turned upside down. We had a new manager who had come up from Disneyworld in Florida. He wore Brooks Brothers suits in which he looked dumpy and untailored compared to the smart look of the tall, fit outgoing manager who wore suits which squeezed tightly around his frame. The new man had an Eastern accent, probably from New York but I think that I attributed all accents that weren't southern to New York at that time so it could have been from anywhere.

He had a very prominent nose and, I suppose, a very common name, Doug Smith, though Smith was not that common in Montana, so it seemed to be more a title than a name and that made him seem even more of an outsider.

He began his tenure quietly, much like a spy. I learned that I was not the only one there who felt like I was being spied upon as I became privy to the world of the desk clerks. Prior to his arrival, their world though so physically close to my own, was in another universe. But, as their suspicions of the new manager grew, I was now an invited guest on planet toil as they complained about new procedures that were being adopted, which were the old procedures before the outgoing manager had changed them. It was going to make us all "look bad" as the outgoing manager and his wife, the assistant manager had managed to manipulate everything from room rates to rates of occupancy and going back to the old system would expose us as failures. I had to chuckle at their use of the inclusive pronoun "us". I had never been made to feel as part of anything they were doing. It was only then that I recognized that I was one of the only, if not the only, employee there who had not been corrupted by the corruption of the system.

I had been fired at one point for doing precisely what one of the favoured bellmen had been doing when I showed up to take over his shift. He had been sitting in a small crowd watching an arm-wrestling competition that was being held in the hotel. He had instructed me to hang out there in case someone needed something. I had only been employed there for a week or so and when a lady approached me and told me to get to work, I replied that I was working. Her reply was a stern look. I would find out later that the lady was the manager's wife and the assistant manager of the hotel. I was fired the next day.

A bit of begging and a piece of logic got me my job back the day after that. After pleading my case to the front desk manager, I was asked, "If you were rehired, would you do a better job?" I replied, "Not with the training that I have been given." She replied that I would be trained properly and that she had noted a certain failing in that department. A couple of days after I was rehired, I realized that she and the head bellman were at odds and the rehiring might have had as much to do with a kind of power struggle as with anything I had to say. But this was all about to change.

A short time after Doug Smith arrived, he began to explain his "spying" he said that he never wanted to make decisions based on assumptions. He said, "Managers should be observers first and actors second." It seemed to make sense, but I knew that he knew that his words would comfort only a few. And, sure enough, a couple of slouches were already talking about making their departure about a week after Doug arrived and even a couple of department managers were notably absent within a few weeks.

It became obvious the Doug favoured the bellmen and this was something that was resisted. He was incorporating professionalism into our world, and this was absolutely foreign to us. Before he came there were no expectations. One was just as likely to find a bellman napping in one of the many hiding spots in the hotel as attending customers at the Front Desk. We had pagers so this wasn't usually a major problem, but it wasn't exactly a model of professionalism.

I thought his methods appropriate and I really began to buy into them after he hired a new chef, invited the bell staff to dine, comment and learn. He also made us write down the amount of tips we were making and told us he was going to give us one technique that would increase our income 100%. Rather than be kind of "gofers" where we were at the behest of the whims of the front desk clerks, we were given a purpose, customer service. We were to spend all of our time in front of the desk attending to customers. Our position at the hotel had been elevated to number two, right below him, and he said that we were more important than he was and if we were to out earn him, he was doing his job because that would reflect a fact; the fact that customer service was elevated to the number one priority. If we were getting tipped to the point that we were driving fancy cars and wearing expensive clothes, that would mean that the hotel was prospering under his tutelage.

This was very confusing at first. There was still a bit of resistance despite that fact that every bellman was making more than the 100 % increase that he promised. A couple of the cool guys who abused the job ended up moving on as they really didn't need the money and certainly did not favour working for it. The people who replaced them seemed to buy in to the system immediately; it was predictable. It was due to the fact that we trained them and set standards without needing any real intention. It was so automatic that one of them seemed to have been there for years after only two or three days on the job. Doug was setting up a system and empowering people. He had empowered us to resist the whims of the mostly bored but sometimes overworked desk staff who made themselves busy by making us busy cleaning the ashtrays in the lobby and such while leaving the customers largely ignored. He assured us that these things would be better done by housekeeping. And lo and behold, maintenance tasks were assigned to maintenance, and he was empowering folks in that department as well. Guests should leave a dollar per night for housekeeping, in his model, and cards subtly reminding guests of the "above and beyond" services rendered would be left on beds after they were made. We might not have known it, but we were just following the basic standards for a Sheraton.

I was promoted to manager of guest services, which had previously been titled bell captain, and this did not make any waves with the rest of the staff. In addition to the added responsibilities of scheduling and such, I was expected to cover in the absence of a scheduled bellman, which was probably why this could seem unattractive to the others. I suppose we were still treating the job as the minimum wage plus tips that it earned us rather than something that could become a career.

Doug, and he was insistent on us calling him that rather than the Mr title the former manager had expected, would regularly call me in to the office for casual chats and welcome me any time I popped in. This was completely different than the couple that he had replaced. The former head insisted on going through layers, including his wife, a kind of phony chain of command that kept him aloof and out of the loop. Doug did make me uncomfortable though; he rarely spoke during the encounters as he would stare into me, giving me looks that I read as incredulous, as though everything that I said needed explaining.

During one of these spontaneous meetings, I just couldn't go on. I said, "You know, I am not going to come in here anymore. All you do is to stare at me like I am some sort of fool." He did not flinch. I had used the word "fool" intentionally for emphasis and maybe shock value.

He replied that I must think him a fool if I thought he had nothing better to do than to listen to me. I am sure I was expecting to be fired. He continued with his reasoning saying that a good manager should listen 90% and speak 10. Because if he was willing to tell folks what to do based on what he thought was going on rather than what was, he was a fool.

I began wishing that word fool didn't exist as he spelled out his reasoning in what remained of his 10 percent. He had put a value on me that I had never even imagined existed. And then he dropped a kind of a bomb. He asked me if I was interested in becoming a hotel manager. "You could become the youngest general manager in the history of the Sheraton corporation."

This was so far from my "plans" of becoming a lawyer and whatever else I thought I had intended to do that I almost immediately deterred him with a resounding "NO!" which must have sounded to him like "that's disgusting". He agreed, telling me but minimizing all of the incredible benefits of his job and told me that it was fabulous that I had such lofty goals, essentially saying I was too good for such a job. I was relieved. But then he broke his 10% rule by continuing and telling me that in life we set patterns and without even knowing it, we follow them. He was probably conscious that he was well into 11 or 12%, breaking a pattern he had set for himself, when he bid me what was probably for him good riddance and for me a relief.

I am not a lawyer. Far from that, I have bobbed around in life like the proverbial cork in the ocean. It took me about forty years to realize that I had given a "no" to almost every positive opportunity that I have ever been offered. And when I have made exceptions, saying "yes" has always resulted in a positive. I have always managed to temper this by making the positive situation short term. Go figure… Failed artist! An artist at failing! The pattern is complete. I have achieved the destiny that I worked so hard to achieve.

Appearances (Act I Scene I)

As I peer around the small space which has become my gallery, objectively judging which work is most reflective of me, I recognize that this would be the canvases upstairs in my tiny studio that I avoid as I type. I wonder if my failure to "complete" them is the product of a mentality that allows me to call them unfinished. One cannot fail in what one has not done.

I hadn't done a painting in weeks though I had a beautiful blank canvas waiting. It had begun to bother me with its emptiness. It seemed to shout whenever I passed and I began moving it around, strategically placing it behind other paintings and such so that it would stop bothering me. It was not that I had no ideas, I am nearly always flush with them, I sketch and play with watercolours constantly, so it wasn't as though I was falling out of practice. But I hadn't done a canvas in what seemed like a very long time and as I looked at the stacks of the unsold orphans surrounded me; I began to wonder about the necessity of creating yet another abstract work.

But the white canvas was taking on a life of its own and bits of it would appear brilliantly anytime that I would move anything in the dankness of my tiny studio. It seemed it was the only thing that would attract the natural light. It then began absorbing that of the electric bulbs. It was as though it was drinking every last bit of illuminating energy out of any ray that had the audacity to penetrate the darkness there. What was to be done?

"What would a successful artist do?" I asked myself.

I tried to hearken to the soul for which I claim to create.

41

"I will finish you one day," I said to the brilliance of the white canvas. "I will."

With this I promised that this promise will be broken as most promises are meant to be...

Appearances (Act I Scene II)

I shook up a woman the other day. She is an unmarried mother who prides herself on sleeping with men who are in relationships, usually married men, and fancies that they sleep with her because of her cuteness and her prowess as a lover. I asked her, "Do you know why men get married?" She did not reply but rather smiled. "So, they can cheat on their wives," I said. I am not sure what she thought was coming as she rarely understands my humour but when I fed her the punch line, she looked as though she had been punched. She saw no humour in it, and I suppose none was intended. I was surprised at her reaction though. She usually entertains herself by stealing the humour from a "joke" by making me explain. This was not necessary in this case.

The more I am honest, the more I feel that honesty is the curse of the dull. It makes life tiresome and tedious. Honesty is an abstract reality and is for those who live in the abstract. Realism is for those who weaponize it; they profess their undying love for their wives and kids on social media and such while cheating on them without regard to anything but than their own egos...

Appearances (Act II Scene I)

I felt the canvas drawing me into a world of humility. Its desire to humiliate me by forcing me to put paint on it was strong. I felt a grand temptation to paint a floral image to satiate my desire to rob it of some of its white brilliance. "Flowers are safe." I tell myself, "Every artist has done them."

Even the greatest of failures have succeeded in painting their rendition of a pot, a basket, or a landscape.

"Why does an artist paint?" I ask myself.

"So, he can cheat on himself," I reply. My honesty keeps the canvas clean and the brushes dry.

The canvas was holding its own in a kind of Jenga game I had created. I would move it to one place and could immediately feel the imbalance that could topple the entirety of the puzzle that my life had become. One can only strategize for so long without making a move. Making the wrong move however...

Explain Yourself Boy! Hecklers of the world unite!

People want to find meaning in everything and everyone. That's the disease of our age.

Pablo Picasso

One of the wonders of abstract art is the fact that normally intelligent folks feign attempts at making some kind of sense out of it. They don't truly want to understand anything; it is just their way of saying, "I get it! You can't draw." Some plead ignorance as they air their contempt. Others take a more offensive approach. Their denial of my existence as an artist is not complete unless they ignore anything I have created after insisting that I show them an example of my work.

There are even those who take it upon themselves to represent me to a third party at a later date, using the "fact" that I did not explain my work to them as proof that it is meaningless and probably just more evidence that I don't have the talent to make exact replications of photos and such so I just slop paint around and pretend.

My body of work, like any failed artist's, contains much more than one genre as anyone with a semblance of a survival instinct could know; whether I like it or not, economics dictates that I chase an alternative audience from time to time. The doubt that seeps into my abstract world often flows out as impressionism, realism, and other genres as I attempt to create marketable items. This is usually the result of a conversation with a goal post mover, who advises me to paint everything from paintings of popular sports figures to catch the public's eye to western scenes to take advantage of my Montana roots. As the goalposts move every time I complete something which the mover claims he can sell, I am applauded for my accomplishment. When the pieces do not sell but rather end up decorating that person's business or personal space, I am advised to return to the abstract and encouraged to create something brilliant which will bring me fame and fortune.

I take this bait from time to time though the only fish it has ever caught is me; the advisor normally manages to weasel a couple paintings out of the deal to decorate his space, a kind of consulting fee for the invitation to the hopscotch game I have been drawn into. The plus side to this is that I have been able to create a body of work for those who believe that I create abstract works for lack of artistic talent, and I have managed to repossess most of the paintings. Folks can witness that I have skills, at least enough to make a piece of work which contains objects that they can recognize. BUT there are folks who can be adamant! Their denial of my ability to create is complete. Therefore, they must encourage me to repent from the evil ways of the abstract and work on my drawing skills without even looking at anything I have created! I am no longer surprised when an adult, much like a child trying to avoid eating vegetables, physically twists her or his head away from something that I am trying to show them. "I cannot understand your paintings!" they exclaim while avoiding the image I am offering, especially when the image is something easily identifiable.

Often when asked to explain my art, I feel I have been given a kind of homework assignment. The untitled must be titled and every picture does not tell a story but rather needs one. And folks can be very clever. At an outing with some artists celebrating the art community, a "fellow artist" asked me what my absolute favourite piece of work is. Now, in this artist friendly environment, I could not have expected the usual sniping that goes on, but I guess I should have. After I showed him a piece that was on display in the presidential suite at the JW Marriott here in Hanoi, I mentioned that it was on display when the US President was visiting. He gave that a very firm sigh of boredom, a yawn. After failing to impress him with this, I made the mistake of showing him a piece that I truly love. It is a piece that was once described by an artist's girlfriend as a masterpiece. Several other folks have expressed very optimistic opinions about it and when I have had it on display at exhibitions, it attracted quite a bit of attention and a couple of offers that, to this day, I cannot believe I did not take.

In my delusional state, I thought that the "fellow artist" would be something other than the snide "compettytor" that nearly every other artist I have ever met is. This "fellow artist" asked what was on my mind when I created it. I told him that it was based on the colour of the wind and what I see when riding my motorcycle at speed. He said, and I hate to say of course but I should have seen it coming, "You must have been imagining crashing. Huh huh, huh huh." I pretended it to be a good-natured comment, meant for a laugh, but I immediately recognized his expertise. You see, most folks will choose a painting they might find interesting or in need of explanation but being a "fellow artist", he went right for the throat. A victory for the art community!

Wine Throw 2017 *Bordeaux and Oil on Canvas 80 cm x 60 cm* **Color of the Wind Collection**.

A Picture is Worth 1000 Words

The failed artist often finds himself honouring the opinion of folks who wouldn't know the difference between a handful of glitter and an ounce of gold dust.

As an explanation of my work, I normally want to go into a long tiring soliloquy and say something like, "the canvas is a cloth, usually made out of some kind of cotton that they stretch around a frame, usually made of cheap wood which will warp at some point. The canvas is woven, and it must be treated with something, gesso, or acrylic paint, so that it is primed, and paint is on its surface rather than absorbed into it. I squeeze some sort of paint, usually oil based, on the canvas and take a pallet knife and move it around until I feel that a piece is finished. Then I display it in public so that I can make asinine explanations about it."

Or I want to give them a play by play: "First I put on the yellow then I go the blue... Then I..."

Recently, I have begun to describe painting as a process. Processes can be understood. Processes are routine. Processes slow things down and murder the creativity that otherwise must be denied. Hopes must be quashed. Failure must be complete. If the creative process can be broken down to a series of mundane acts, which suck the creativity out, the process can be understood. The elemental bullying that one must suffer to be a complete failure can be the success. One must be dogged in one's attempts to fail. One must be relentless.

Some of the moments I most cherish are when I have a person, usually a very attractive female, a trophy wife* of one of the potential buyers at a place, ask question after question and then say something like "No one would know that if you did not explain that." In other words: I just wasted your time. HAHAHAHA! Did you really think I was interested?

There is nothing so intimate as sharing a few precious words with such an individual. There's nothing that screams "idiots" more than having two of them in a discussion of the creative. And yes, it is plural for a reason. She may be an idiot for asking the questions, but I am definitely an idiot for replying.

I read somewhere that the term "askhole" describes a person who asks a question about something they don't know with no interest whatsoever in the answer. I have met quite a few askholes in my short life. The most pertinent are those who compare a particular painting to the most recognized artist in a certain area; abstract-Pollock, surreal-Dali, impressionist-Monet... They determine that I was influenced by one artist or another and then put that in question form. They are sometimes worlds away. If I have the unmitigated gall to correct them in any way, they return to their childhood for a round of pouting. But, as they are usually accompanied by one of the above-mentioned trophy wives, their ego can be restored by standing next to him or her.

One of the hidden talents of the beautiful and seemingly stupid: Perhaps the same gene that makes them lack interesting things to say gives them the good sense to know when to keep their mouth shut. This is something that most of the ostensibly intelligent folks that I know could use. Like the author of this story for example.

*I am using the word "wife" here due to expediency. Most of the families that I know, gay or straight, refer to one of the members as a "wife." And most, probably all of the folks I know with trophy wives or husbands, also have trophy girlfriends and boyfriends and it is not un-common that these relationships cross genders. In other words, a man can have a wife, trophy or not, and a trophy boyfriend. And, when this is the case, it usually works to the artist's benefit, and I am stereotyping here, as these fellows often have an excellent background in all that is art so...And to be fair, some of the ladies who take ex-ception to my work, make entirely relevant comments. But it is me who is doing the writing here and they know who they are! So, they can seek me out for an apology... And buy a painting while they are at it!

Expecting truth or honour from a man who is having relations with your wife is like expecting clean water from a sewer.

Reduced to Madness

One recognizes one's madness in the sanity of others. Nietzsche wrote something to the effect that "Madness, while being rare in individuals, in certain epochs in societies it is the rule." An artist's madness comes not from living outside of the norm but rather the failure to accept the norm. Not in such a way that one dresses and acts like one believes an artist is supposed to dress and act. This is conforming to the norm. Appearing to conform to the norm while being beyond caring about what is mad or normal and recreating one's image of the world free of consideration as to that which could be considered insane or sane is the only time one is truly creating.

Failure to Understand

I have become immune to the pathetic, the petty, the pedantic... In doing so, I suppose I have become the very personification of those three words. I could see, that, as a failed artist, I had no reason for success. After all, the admission of failure has to be the first, biggest step on the road to success! You see, or at least I do, failure is an integral part of success. It is like trying. "If at first you don't succeed, try, try again!" Why bother succeeding the first time when there was all that trying to be had. And try one must on the road to success. To fail, one must try. And try as one might, success is not just around any corner, it must be found through a series of failures! This is not unlike one who is lost in the woods. Looking up only gets one a better view of the tree branches. Looking down nets one a great sense that one is indeed grounded. A look from side to side is insurance that one is surrounded by an insurmountable set of obstacles that can neither be moved nor mowed down. Yet there remains a trail, a hope, and it is hope that dies last. One who wishes to succeed need only to persist in the belief that there is no such thing as lost. The more disappointment, the sweeter success will be when one finds it! Logic would have it no other way. It makes sense that the road to failure is filled with a god-awful lot of success. But one must learn to recognize success. Like most blessings in life, it comes in disguise.

I was teaching a literature course a few years ago and I was going to have my students produce a piece of work. They were a small gang of wannabe nerds, mostly bespectacled, with goggle like glasses that had little or no correction but were rather part of an ensemble intended to give them the air of the aloof, which they believed true nerds to be.

They were to produce two scenarios of a same event. In the first scenario, they were to compose a piece about a heroic character who, against all odds, could succeed in a seemingly impossible situation. They were quite excited about the prospects of this. Harry Potter was all the rage at the time, and I could sense an energy filling the room as they went about muttering and mumbling about a new superhero that they would create to conquer situations so impossible that one could only dream them. I didn't mean to be dramatic when I dropped the other shoe, but I waited. When I recognised that they were all settled into the first part of the task, I introduced the second scenario. They were to have the same protagonist fail when he or she was absolutely destined to win.

I remember saying, "Just as your character must be able to snatch victory from the jaws of defeat, he, she, or it, must also be able to snatch defeat from the jaws of victory."

I suppose if I were a more honest man, I would admit that the students were doing a bit of my homework for me. At that time, I had been composing an intended novel in the mornings before I would head off to my job at the school where I was teaching them. I was averaging about 1000 words per day, and when I say about, I could almost say exactly. I had become so proficient at unconsciously estimating my word count that I would finish my daily passages about 10 or 11 words on either side of one thousand if not precisely at 1000. While this was a source of pleasure and pride initially, I began to think of it as a curse. It seemed as though my writing was contrived, as though I had some sort of mental counter that was requiring me to produce a numerically correct amount of gibberish just so that I could hit a mark on a word count. And try as I might, I could not get myself to produce any more or any less. I have been writing for quite some time and I have experienced that which is known as "writer's block," but I was not quite sure what this would be called. Writer's meter? That might be it. I always felt that writing should be an adventure, yet here I was writing as if I was adding change to a parking meter. It was as though I was taking the same taxi every morning to the same place with the same driver. Creativity be damned, it had begun to feel like a job.

I empathized with the students as they hemmed and hawed. I took it as a sign of the depth of thinking that was required to complete the incredible assignment that I had bestowed upon them. It was captivating and worthy of complete concentration. I wondered whether they were worthy. They seemed to think so. Could it be true? Or could this simply be attributed to the arrogance of the young.

But as the hemming and hawing continued, I became less confident that their considerations were about the thinking involved but rather the length of the final product. And... Predictably came the first question.

"How long do they have to be?"

"Who are they?" I replied.

My attempt at academic humour went unnoticed.

"The essays!" they whined.

"One thousand words." I replied.

I suppose I was a bit indignant. I was bothered by the fact that they did not understand that 1000 words should always show on the meter at the end of a daily sojourn into literary greatness.

"Roughly five paragraphs."

"Do you mean you want a five-paragraph essay or 1000 words?"

"Whichever brings your journey to an end," I said. This was intended as sage, and I probably added a wink. I don't know when the winking started but I can say that if anyone finds winking bothersome, they should use caution when mocking another's winking as I am sure that this is how I picked it up in the first place.

The discussion which had quelled after they had begun writing their first piece recommenced and I wondered if I had done the right thing, adding the "enrichment exercise" to their initial assignment. I became concerned as a sense of doubt was taking hold of me. I calmed myself with the thought that there were at least 70 minutes left in the double period so there was plenty of time to murder.

I suppose one of the greatest challenges of instructing anyone to do anything is knowing when the hell to shut up. I don't know how many times I have delivered an introduction to a pretty cool assignment only to ruin it after having said something clever and been rewarded with a chuckle or one of those admiring gleams that the young can give so lovingly when one says or does something pleasing. The same look that one receives when giving a bottle to a hungry toddler, a kind of primal display of the appreciation of satisfaction that never leaves us though it evolves with time. One needs to know when enough is enough, probably the toughest of lessons to learn.

"Can we just choose one?"

This cry came from the mouthiest of the pack and after waiting to see if I would bite, her whine became a chorus.

"Can we just choose one?"

"No! You can't!"

The words dived out of my mouth. I was escalating!

"Ah come on! Do you want quality or quantity? "

This questionable reasoning came from the most slovenly of the nerds.

"Come on?" He whined.

And here I had done it. The tiny victory that I had achieved with the hero assignment had been snatched away with the addition of the loser. I recognized then that I had just written an essay for them. But I would be damned if I was going to let them know it.

Snatching defeat from the jaws of victory has been my stock in trade for the better part of my life. My mother often uses the expression, "Can't win for losin'." And she usually supplements this rousing gift with another inspirational jibe, "That's right, always a day late and a dollar short." Referring to me...of course. I mean, what better way to raise a kid than letting him know very well that losing is the best part of his game and that failure would become his art.

The Saboteur

He stole this story right out from under me... or maybe she did. Whoever took it...it was sabotage, plain and simple. But there is no plain and simple in sabotage. This is why one must first look in a mirror when one is looking for a saboteur.

Artsy

Here I was, yet again in an airport. One of the things that I despise about travel is the personas that people take on while in airports and on planes. It is as though everyone believes that they own an individual space which all others are intent on invading. People take on ridiculous airs as though the very air in the airport fills their heads with an exaggerated sense of self-importance.

Just then, I saw her approaching. I recognized her.

"My goodness but she is fetching." I mumbled to myself.

My English has improved with my travels, fetching is a word of the elite.

"An Aussie" I thought, "but maybe a Kiwi. Was she a parent of one of my students?"

"Oh no… That's who she is! She is that beautiful woman from the lacquer painting class."

Shoulder length brown hair perfectly coiffed to expose the exquisite lines of her beautiful visage, she had one of those faces designed to smile. She would never age; added years would do nothing but further expose her grace.

My ego told me she was looking right at me as she scurried in my direction on her perfectly sculpted legs. I looked around to see what she was really looking at. I returned my gaze to her and noted that her blouse was open just wide enough to classily expose a bit of cleavage.

"Victoria's Secret," I thought; I could sense just a hint of her lacy brassiere. She was looking at me, seeking me. I struggled to raise my eyes to meet hers as she closed the distance. She is heading my way.

"Luck!" I thought. "Good luck. We are going to be on a flight together. Yes. And I had not checked in yet. Luck. We would arrange it. We would sit together. We would discuss art. That's what we would do. Of course."

"Are there any galleries in Phnom Penh?" I would say, "Well we certainly will find out!" she will reply. Everything we will say will be accentuated with a duet of affectionate giggles. "A hotel reservation? Of course not. Where are you staying?" Our imaginary conversation worked its way through my mind as my adrenaline rushed. Big smile. She is almost here. I return her smile as I now know hers is for me.

"Hey!" She says with a beautiful ANZAC accent. Ok. It is one or the other, but I know not which. I can't tell the difference. I will ask, a talking point.

"How you going?" She asks.

"To Cambodia", I reply clumsily.

"Great! I hope you love it there."

She has a different destination. "I haven't bought my ticket yet." I added with a bit of a squeak. Disappointment mixed with hope.

"I'm going home!" She said "So excited! I haven't been in years."

"Where is home?"

"Auckland." It sounded like Oakland. The rein of confusion had begun.

I was not yet versed in the geography of that part of the world or any for that matter and "Auckland" sounded like it should be in Australia or maybe next to San Francisco.

"New Zealand!" she continued. She was undoubtedly reading the word stupid tattooed on the front of my skull. A Persian friend of mine once told me that I had one of those faces that could be read much like a book. I remember him telling me this was some kind of gift. This may be true, but I was hoping she could turn some pages as she was obviously stuck on the one which read: "stupid."

"Oh yes of course!" I said "My friend Wayne has invited me there several times. Your country must be gorgeous."

"Well, I wouldn't call it my country exactly. I was born and raised an Aussie."

"Downhill" I thought. "That is where this is going. And now I have an uphill battle. And neither my legs nor my jaw will get me up the hill. The hoof in my mouth will prevent this."

"It's ok." She smiled or maybe I should say she continued to smile. She seemed excessively happy to see me. If I was a more perceptive person, I could have known her grin was certainly hiding something; something she could not wait to reveal.

"Wow! It has been a long time since I last saw you! I certainly enjoyed your work," I said.

"I am surprised! I am surprised you remember!"

"Oh certainly. You are not exactly forgettable" I cooed. I believed I had delivered a line worthy of Bogart or Brando.

"Really??? I am surprised you can remember anything!"

Her grinning was getting annoying. I felt as though she was sucking the brain out of my head. I wanted to tell her to stop. I suppose a quizzical look replaced the stupid one and she must have thought I was ready for an explanation.

"Well, you are certainly looking good, man! Healthy I mean."

Relief. I would have exhaled but I was too busy sticking my chest out and holding my stomach in. It was at this time I noted that she had a Premier Class tag on her carry on.

"You know, we really missed you when you stopped coming to class."

"I still came on weekends," I said.

I was becoming defensive. In reality, even my weekend visits had ceased. I wanted to take this back as I knew a compliment was on its way. After all, I was the only male in the class and the teacher's pet to boot. And our instructor was one of the greatest living lacquer painters, a national treasure in Vietnam. Hell! I had even dated the teacher's daughter, an accomplished artist herself.

"We used to take bets!" She continued.

Her joy was immeasurable. Her smiling face momentarily seemed somehow demonic and cruel.

"Yep! We used to bet on you!"

"Worthy of a wager I was!" I thought. Relief once again; oh, what I would give to heave a heavy sigh. "But bet? On what?"

She let me take it in for what seemed an eternity and then after apparently recognizing I was not clever enough to ask on what, she threw out her clue!

"We would bet on when you would fall off your stool!"

Crashing it came. Crashing down on me, all of a sudden. Here I stood in my ego driven talent laden pose, waiting with great expectations for her declarations of her admiration of my work, my artistic talent and it was my drunkenness that impressed her. And I suppose she must have bet in favour of my ability to balance as she seemed positive, even if was in a contemptuous way.

As she scurried away, the volume of her laughter increased in that hollow hell of an airport. As the distance between us grew, I recognized that I was beyond shame. I was ready for a second helping of grief. Could she not return for an encore?

I don't recall ever falling off my stool though I must have come close. I am certain I lost consciousness regularly as I endured those hours in my drunken inferno. I was most likely brought back to life by my head bouncing off my worktable not unlike a boxer who is awakened by his head hitting the canvas after a hard KO punch. It was due to the grace of God that I never wore a lacquer painting home on my forehead on one of those dark days. The lady had left me wondering if I had ever showed up even close to sober.

I suppose shock would best describe my state as I suffered sobriety on the plane to Phnom Penh. I recalled my anguish on those mornings, toiling away after drunken sleepless nights. I took long toilet breaks, falling asleep on but not quite falling off the throne. I was sometimes perched in such a way that I could prop my head against the door, but it was a dangerous reach so I would crush myself against the side of the stall to spend a precious moment or two in the world of the unconscious. I could remember scouting out the stall that had the most toilet paper on the roll so that I could rest my head on its softness. This the ladies did not see but they certainly could imagine.

My time at the table painting was not so different but, in my drunkenness, I believed it to be. The suave dedicated artist I fancied myself was to her crowd a stinking drunken man wobbling back and forth on his three-legged stool, not in an overly imbibed display of dedication but rather as a spectacle, like a teetering drunk in the bleachers at a sports contest.

I thought of her and her crew when we were at cruising altitude.

"Envy!" I decided. "They all envied me. Jealousy must be a hard pill to swallow. She is probably having a difficult time deciding what to wash it down with right now, looking through some menu in the first-class cabin in that crappy plane she is on."

"Looking?" I thought as my eyes strode elegantly through the pay for what you drink menu on the low budget airline I was flying. Not me. "Peruse" I thought. "I am perusing the menu. That's what folks like me do." If there was anything alcoholic other than beer on the menu, I am sure I would have ordered. It had been months since I had a drink but after that shellacking, I thought I deserved a few.

Failure (Scattered Shouts)

They will tell you that failure is not an option. That is ridiculous. Failure is always an option. Failure is the most readily available option at all times... But it is a choice. You can choose to fail. You can choose to succeed.

Chael Sonnen

Appearances (Act II Scene II)

Why was this canvas so crucial? Why did it fill me with fear? Was I afraid not to fail? Dare I say succeed? I decided that the canvas had it in for me. It was pushing to an end. Going further was past the point. There is no point.

I have always loved the challenge of the abstract. There are days when I am completely in love with life as I create one new thing after another. I look around at things I have created. I feel a calmness rush through me. That is what I have come to know as my inner peace. Creation is yoga for my soul.

If earning a living wasn't a necessity, I would have no problem filling canvases or any other surface that seemed in need of colour and a bit of my soul. But life rears its ugliest of heads whenever I feel like I need to take an inventory. And my inventory of canvases untouched was one.

The most difficult thing for me, when I am creating, is knowing when I am finished. I was recalling a time when I hosted a live show at my gallery when the artist set out a row of blank canvases on the pristine fakeness of the artificial grass which covered the floor. As his show began, he carelessly squeezed out acrylic paint from the plastic condiment bottles he was using. I noted more the paint splatter that flew off the canvas onto the floor, one careless colour after another, than anything that hit its mark. It was a bit depressing to me, but I tried not to grimace as the event was being filmed and the others in the small audience were obviously playing along. I played along. I did notice one woman who looked more puzzled than curious as he began rolling around on the canvases using his body as his brush. And I suppose seeing a grown man squirming around in a puddle of paint wearing nothing but an undergarment, which looked much like a diaper, was as new to her as it was to me.

After his demonstration was finished, we had a session of song and drinking and more song and more drinking. The video team participated and then staged a kind of questions-and-answer debriefing. The audience was meant to ask leading questions and the artist would reply. I thought it awfully contrived but I played along. I could not help but ask, and I knew it would be a softball question, how he determined when he was finished. Unfortunately, I could have answered my own question as one often can when one witnesses something that is contrived though meant to be creative. "That is my energy there." he said through the translator as he pointed to the canvases. The translator, who happened to be the puzzled woman, appeared to be recovering from her shock.

"When my energy was gone," he said rather dramatically, "I was finished."

I did my best to wear the face of sincerity that I sometimes do but I am sure the camera caught the transition from sarcasm to disbelief only to end at scorn. I suppose I felt a bit of contempt coming in my direction as well and I suspected the Q&A would be edited carefully.

"So much for a spontaneous performance", I thought.

As we left the gallery to head out for some roast duck at a restaurant nearby, I was wondering who was going to clean my gallery. I wondered if that energy that was gone was going to resurface when he and his crew returned to pick up his paintings.

I was not the only one who wondered this. I ran into the translator lady a few months later. I was in the thickest part of the maze that makes up the Old Quarter here in Hanoi looking for one of the more famous upscale Vietnamese restaurants, which are usually "hidden gems". They huddle among the street stands with the most obscure addresses possible, much like the studios of the wealthy artists here. They like to give off the air of "authentic" rags to riches successes as their lavish accoutrements stand in stark contrast to the mom-and-pop places which surround them.

The translator, whose name I would learn was Huong, happened to be sitting with a couple of other stylish ladies in one of the popular cafes that use sidewalk seating as the overflow on busy nights. I heard my name being screamed and I recognized her when she flew out in front of me and blocked my path. I said the appropriate "Nice to see you again." and such with the intention of continuing on my way but she was insistent in her polite invitation to sit with her and her friends, so I did. She had hardly finished introducing them when she asked me about the cleaning. She was speaking rapid fire, in Vietnamese, to the ladies at the table and I nodded knowingly as I understood everything except her words. Her histrionic body language was an attempt at replicating the man's act without actually flopping around on the sidewalk and she did well in her imitation. She stopped long enough to ask about the cleaning and barely let me speak, apparently correctly guessing the answer. She gave the table a wipe or two and a stiff pounding for emphasis. And I gave it a healthy scrubbing to let them know she was right without interrupting her rant.

She bid farewell to her friends rather suddenly and offered me a lift to the restaurant, which everyone at her table said they knew, despite their ignorance of its geographical location. On her fashionable antique Vespa scooter, we putted among the pedestrian traffic. When we arrived at the restaurant, I invited her in. She informed me that she would not be eating. I guessed that she had earned her chops as a translator in an official government position as everything that she said sounded like a declaration. She said that she would come in but only because it is impolite to allow someone to eat alone!

It was more than a little awkward. I ordered dishes meant for sharing but she declined everything. I don't think she even took a sip of the tea that she ordered. As she began to unveil her motivation for beckoning me on the street, I began to feel even more uncomfortable. She was there to make a point. Her desire was to affirm the fact that she had also wanted to ask the question which I had. She guessed that I thought the artist's answer was "phony". I sensed that something was awry. She wanted to know if she had read the look on my face correctly. I knew that she wanted something truthful as she promised that she would keep it between her and me.

I have been interviewed many times for jobs but rarely for anything art related. When I have been interviewed, I have always had the grace to be gracious and thankful to have been invited to an interview or an exhibit. Though it was not an interview, I felt a bit of pressure to get the answer just right. I was trying to formulate a short quip to get by with something clever, but the intensity of her stare had me off guard and I had to fall back on my truth.

And I formally introduced this by saying, "To tell you the truth," which any listener should understand to be my truth followed by the usual pack of lies that seem to escape my lips anytime I try to tell my truth. There is no getting around it. I aim to please. I thought I was agreeing that his answer was indeed "phony" though in his case phony meant sincere as he himself was a phony so saying phony things came natural to him and that meant it was genuine.

I don't remember my exact words, but I know they were a good deal harsher than I intended. The look on her face was absolutely comical. I burst out laughing. I had been talking with my mouth full and I felt a little bit of food escaping. I was not embarrassed. She seemed too busy "taking it all in" to let a few random chunks of food get in the way of her shock. I realized then that she was not expecting my truth and I was supposed to clarify what should have been a compliment and that my reading of her look at my studio was completely incorrect. Even I have a couple of groupies and to them I can do no wrong. And she was one of the diaper clad artist's groupies. Everything that I had assumed was completely incorrect.

The look on her face during the Q & A at the gallery was shock. She was appalled that I had questioned his abilities.

Her grabbing me out of the crowd that evening was not her giving me a chance to explain but rather her opportunity to condemn me. It was her way of saying, "How dare you?".

The cleaning conversation with the ladies was her explaining to her friends my lack of appreciation for art. I was more concerned about the clean-up!

My repetition of her scrubbing was my confession that she was right.

The ride to the restaurant was but a hand to the bewildered, she knew that a fool who could not recognize the greatness of one of her idols, could never be trusted to be left alone on the streets and even less so in someone's place of business. She was being what Western journalists in North Korea call "a minder".

Her refusal to eat was contempt. She would be cursed to starvation before she would eat with such a lout.

Her asking me the question was a last chance at redemption.

My reply was a last straw.

I knew my commentary would get back to the artist in one form or another as the woman with whom I was now seated had come to my gallery as the artist's translator. I also recalled that she had assured our conversation was between "me and you" meaning me and her and whenever I hear this, I know that that means "Tell me something you don't want me to share so I can share it."

Needless to say, I haven't heard from any of that crew, and I probably never will.

I arranged and rearranged the dishes, and I repeatedly offered them to her to avoid replying to any more questions. But the pause had become too pregnant. Her anger had been incubating for much too long to stop it from revealing itself. No mask can conceal ire.

I decided to risk an explanation, a stab at redemption.

"I can hardly criticize him." I said, "Energy is a hard thing to calculate."

I often find that humility leads to humiliation, yet I could not find it in myself to express anything but that. The successful have no problem expressing opinions and often find it their prerogative not only to demean but destroy with their words. It seems that in the ladder of life those whose tools are sharpest are those at the top and any attempts at achieving a place on their step are cut down like medieval knights severed the ropes of invaders scaling the walls of the castle they were defending. But the meek, who will never inherit any of the earth, with the possible exception of the plot in which they will be buried, must limit their commentary to the positive. And they must be positively appreciative of their inclusion in anything that even resembles an attempt at scaling the walls of success.

Marketing: Those who chew glass...

Those who chew glass won't often listen to those who don't. Those with an appetite for shards of baked sand seldom understand those who don't.

Those who created the internet have created a new world. It has become so easy to reconnect with folks that one hardly need a motive. I ended up calling an acquaintance that I had not seen in about forty years after I saw him online.

"This so crazy," he said. "I was just telling my wife about you the other day. You may not want to admit to this, but I remember that you used to chew glass."

I wondered why I wouldn't and told him so. He continued to express his doubts as, in his thought, folks might want to delete pieces of their life which might not suit their current image. He continued on this line, and I imagined that I was a bit of a shocker as a kid and I thought of but did not mention other incidents, which were at least as forgettable.

Then came the side of the conversation in which I was interested and that was how he was making his way in life. I was right in my assumption, that he was successfully earning his keep in the internet world. And, as I also presumed, he had a wealth of experience in online marketing, which was my motivation for contacting him.

After allowing him a bit of his background, I began grilling him with specific questions about how to sell my art online. I was a bit nonplussed that he was advising me away from selling my art online. He maintained that art was an intimate thing that needed to be experienced face to face… his words.

I was not pleased nor convinced of this, and I mentioned a website that he could have but did not bother looking up, preferring to continue on his line of reasoning.

He pretty much described it as an impossibility to have a successful online gallery. I did not want to be convinced, but rather to convince him so I did not listen any more than he had looked up the website.

I talked over him which was easy to do as there was a kind of delay and I used strategic umms whenever I was at loss for words.

He was not at loss for words. This is his world. As a cyber visitor, I was expected to heed his advice. He instructed much as a tour guide might. There was a maze of details that one would encounter as an online marketer. He informed me that as much as he would like to, he could not recommend online marketing as being effective in selling art.

I had forgotten that he was a very good musician, and he understood his art intimately. And, especially to artists, art is a very individual undertaking. The regular discipline that one needs to practice so they can create is deeply personal. And, according to him, nothing could be less attractive than the soul of an individual being bared in the digital world.

After our conversation, I felt a bit unfulfilled, perhaps as one feels when one has had bad sex. Recognizing that bad sex might be preferable to no sex, that is not a given. I remained unconvinced.

I do not chew glass anymore. I have not for many years. My motives for chewing glass in the first place are not a mystery to me. The desire to chew glass remains in a metaphorical sense. Glass I do not grind but teeth I do. Creating art to sell is not unlike this. There is no nutritive value in the results. As he said and I did not want to hear, art is an intimate thing, one must experience that which nourishes him not what pleases the crowd...

Anyone who doesn't know that water is the best drink in the world has never truly been thirsty

I went off the deep end trying to catch the same fish that I sought in the shallows. I needed to drown so I could find some air that had not been breathed before. I knew madness was temporary. I know sanity to be a curse. Biding my time at the bottom of a bottle and then another; washing my mind free of thought, guilt and then consciousness. I sleep a dreamless sleep. I live a dreamless life. Tortured only by occasional bouts with restlessness, which should have sent me scrambling for opportunity but rather... I woke up in our swimming pool. Dragging me up to where I started, on two legs, I pulled my drenched jeans and underwear down to my ankles and just like that I had myself in leg irons and with neither the desire nor the flexibility to remove them; I trudged towards the studio one uncertain step after another.

In my nakedness I began to create. I don't like painting when I am impaired. Things don't come naturally. I have heard that it should be the opposite, but my experience differs. The Lady in the Forest is an exception. While my girlfriend and our little girl slept safely away from the drunken mess that I had become, I battled.

I pride myself with textures. It is true that much of my work is so much better when one can experience it live. And this is true for most artists despite the excellent photography and the enhancement of the digital world.

The Lady in the Forest began as a conversation as some works do. I was asked to do a commission, a painting of Che smoking a cigar. This was ordered by the lady that would soon be in the forest.

I have often been asked to do a portrait. Usually, it is more of a challenge. My experience as an abstract expressionist has taught me that folks often believe that I cannot recreate that which is real, so I just slop paint onto a canvas.

"I don't understand." I often hear. "What is the story behind the painting?" the more generous say.

The lady was there, in waiting so to speak.

I felt myself bold as I sculpted the lines that would be her beautiful black hair. I was using only pallet knives with which I could feel the subtle form of her body which is anything but subtle. Knowing not her nakedness but aware of my own I prescribed clothing onto her, some familiar items that I would behold when witnessing her beauty and occasionally hugging on to it.

As I moved my tool lovingly, desiring nothing more than her touch, I thought not of the two who slept so soundly above. But I had thought of them, cheatingly, as I imagined one does as they make love blindly, eyes closed, imagining the one or the many that spur the pheromones that harden the soft and make lovemaking a distant pleasure an embodiment of the desire; a kind of masturbation that is often more mutual than can be told.

I died. I had nothing left but an unfinished work. I had nothing left to finish the work. I imagined my father in his workshop; my grandfather in his, the discipline which I had no choice but to be born with. I steeled myself as I drank yet another beer. I felt my innards crying "ENOUGH!" as I guzzled it down.

The lady was waiting. I cried myself to sleep. I cried myself awake. The lady who slept so soundly awoke.

"You must see this." I said to myself. I saw her for the first time. As I stood in front of it, I could feel my father and grandfather next to me. I recognized the strength that I had endured. I lost all of that and became a weeping fool in front of The Lady in the Forest.

The Lady in the Forest (2015) Oil on Canvas 120 cm x 100 cm From *The Mind Garden Collection*

Simple Assault

The police car pulled up without fanfare. The policeman inside hadn't bothered to turn on the lights.

I hadn't given the guy the thrashing that he deserved. I just threw him down on the old concrete sidewalk and bounced his head off it a few times.

The cop came up to ask me what was happening. He seemed a bit surprised at my calm demeanour. Or maybe it was that the guy's wife wouldn't stop screaming and this was shocking him. A couple of neighbours came out. One of them seemed to be prepared to give testimony. She yelled something across the street which stopped the wife from screaming. My wife, my ex-wife now, stood by unconcerned. She looked like she was trying to bring true meaning to the term "aloof," but then again, she knew that I would handle it. She didn't know how.

It was an assault pure and simple, and we were purely and simply in Butte, Montana home of Evel Knievel, the Berkeley pit, and an annual St. Patrick's Day celebration that has grown somewhat famous in the past few years. It is also my father's hometown. I was taking my wife, a Philippine woman, to visit my mother, an American mongrel, in Great Falls. We stopped in Butte to say hi to some relatives and I decided to take the wife up to have a look at the house in which my long dead grandparents used to reside.

A tall, old, wooden fence separated my grandparents' house from the Stewart Mine behind it and it had a workshop and some weird ass dog kennel in the backyard that it shared with my great aunt's house next door. My great

aunt's house was built in the early 1900's and it was bizarre. It looked like a hotel that one could see in a movie
about the Old West, three stories of brick, mounted on a
root cellar, where cat-eating rats the size of mastiffs ruled
if you were to believe what we were told... We did.

My grandparents' house was not bizarre. It is a basic
ranch style home built upon a high concrete basement
sunk into the hillside to compensate for the severe angle
of the hill on which the neighbourhood was built.

But getting back to the assault, before the onset of internet property speculation, the land values had dropped in
Butte to the point that people going to the university there
could buy property for so little that it hardly made sense
to rent. "You can become a homeowner for damn near
free." This is what the victim said anyway. Yes, he was a
student there, a graduate student. He was probably in his
late twenties or early thirties; it was hard to tell. He had a
mountain man beard that would have looked out of place
in New York or Los Angeles or wherever the hell he was
from but apparently, he thought was appropriate for him
in the Big Sky country. He was stroking it when he came
out and down the stairs probably thinking this gave him
some sort of mature or learned appearance but to me it
looked like it itched like hell, and he wished it wasn't on
his face. I was very glad it wasn't on mine.

But anyways, ("anyways" is something that we like to
say there after a digression, so that no one else can get in
a word edgewise, another thing that we like to say). Anyways, I mentioned quickly to my wife that people in
Butte were really friendly and that he would probably ask
us in for coffee, but my instincts were telling me otherwise... they were telling me that this clown was an out of
stater. And... this isn't always so bad except that many

out of staters have this complex that makes them feel like they have to go around insulting the locals, usually behind their backs, to make them certain that they know that the out of stater is not a local hick. Now firstly, in defence of Butte folks, and Montana folks in general, Butte was one of the largest cities west of the Mississippi in its heyday and it still maintains a bit of its cosmopolitan character. For example, while shopping in a couple of its used bookstores, I have found more than a few titles that would be rare in other towns its size. But getting back to the story, this dude comes out to greet me and my wife and a conversation begins. I told him that this was my grandparents' old house and that my grandpa and uncle had worked in the mine. Oh great, he says and starts off on his tangent about housing prices and his studies and whatever the hell else he thought was impressive enough to tell a guy who was dressed more like a lawyer than a miner's grandson, complete with an exotic wife. He seemed to realize that we hadn't really come to listen to his life story and that we truly didn't care whether it was him or any of the other six point something billion inhabitants of the planet who was there, we had just come by to see the house, but he continued talking. When he finally shut up, I mentioned to my wife that my grandpa had been a carpenter and that he had added an addition on to the house to which I pointed. I took a few steps towards the side of the house, still on the public sidewalk, to show her what I was talking about. She followed, as did he. But she stood there smiling and nodding which he did not. He began with a sort of diatribe about the terrible building skills of the person who had added the thing on to side of the house. Granted, the guy was probably right, and I wouldn't have blinked an eye were it not that I had already identified that person as my grandpa. Now, this may seem strange to some but I suddenly suspected that he was armed or that he had a firearm reasonably close. I suspected this for two reasons. One, I knew a local gunsmith who sold his business because he didn't want to sell any more guns to these out of staters who had this exaggerated conception of their property rights and seemed to think that it was just fine to pull a gun on someone as long as that someone was on or near their property. Two, this skinny assed guy had, to my reckoning, probably never been in a fist fight in his life. And the problem with this is, if you have someone posturing aggressively and confidently in a situation where he should at least show a little caution…that person might have a reason for this confidence… For some when they are young this is Mommy, Daddy, or big brother, when the same some get older it is a gun. Well, I was pretty sure that his gun was inside his house as he didn't have a holster and was bouncing around too much for him to have it in the waistband of his pants. I then began to ask him whether he had understood that my grandpa was the builder of the addition. Not only did he smile with glee when I said this, but he continued talking over me and towards my wife. I asked him to go back inside of his house, but he continued ignoring me.

As I told the policeman a story similar to that which I have written above, the neighbour lady helped the bearded wonder back to consciousness and had him sitting propped up against the grey painted concrete wall of the basement that bordered the cracked, chalky sidewalk. I added irrelevant details, of course, just like I did in the story above, but I still didn't feel I had the officer convinced that I was free of guilt. Suddenly, the cop began to speak with a barely detectable Irish lilt. "You're comin' along now." he said. As I looked up at the beaten man's wife, I made a last desperate attempt to avoid incarceration. Mr. Mountain man may have made the conversion, but his wife had his roots written all over her in the form of the tie died hippie smock that she was flaunting for the whole world to see. She had a tooled leather headband as well with a peace sign prominently etched into the front. I changed my tone. I stopped saying "sir" I said, "You see that hippy. Why don't she go in and put on some real clothes?" The officer looked up. "That's what's wrong with this country, people like that don't have any respect. Someone's got to teach 'em some." I said, and to this I added, "Damned hippies. *Pug ma hon!*" Just for effect as I put my hands behind my back awaiting the handcuffs.

The policeman looked at me with what I might describe as glee. Undoubtedly, he didn't have an opinion on hippies either way, but no Irishman can resist the appeal to the ridiculous. I noticed the Irish surname on his name tag. He had already mentioned mine. "So, you cracked his head on the ground didya?" "Ah well..." "Or didya hafta fend 'im offya when he tried ta grabya? Kinda likea swimmer when he's trying to help a drownin' man. Ya kinda pushed 'im offya did ya?" The neighbour looked at the policeman as he winked at her. She stepped off the sidewalk to cross the street on her way back to her house. As he put the handcuffs on, I winced. I don't know why but I felt a tinge of guilt for what I had done. I hadn't done anything like that for a good twenty years. "Hell hates a hippy," I muttered to my wife as we watched the tie dye woman get in her car to follow her husband to the police station. "And so do cops." My wife, to her credit, did not laugh or smile. She left that to my Uncle Jack when I told him the story a few hours later and laugh he did.

87

Eloquence

The bastion of nonsense; the bastard child of profanity. Knitting thoughtless irrelevance to mindless chatter revealing the extent of one's vocabulary and the dearth of one's thought. (When we don't mind it don't matter).

I took a journey into the world of sincerity, the world to which I escape from time to time when the bounty with which my lies reward me loses its value as the gullible make a fool of the fooler. The easy lie makes me lazy and reveals the media fodder that I would become if I was famous. No one with the intelligence level above that of a lizard could believe my lies so I begin to tell the truth in excess. And then, just as my lies have been believed, my truth is rejected. Though this may seem rather logical to those who know the story of the boy who cried wolf, does not the truth relate to something verifiable that we can all discover?

I stood on the porch watching what looked like a monitor lizard swim around a small algae laden pond in front of the beautiful brick house that I had rented. It was much like a brownstone though not as ornate. The brick paved patio in front of the place was large enough and seemingly intended for a car but it was inaccessible to a four wheeled vehicle as are many such entrances here in Ha Noi. It was designed to be accessed by pedestrians and motorbikes along a narrow path that bordered the pond. The bricks of the patio descended into the pond as if the architect had planned it as a dock for a small boat. It would often become the stage for a sort of wildlife drama, as one of the large pond lizards would take down a rat or one of the large fist sized toads that looked more like stones than live animals.

This drama was a bit shocking the first few times I witnessed it, but the shock value had faded. After one lives in a developing country for a while, the shock value of things like rats, roaches, and geckos becomes more a source of curiosity, a kind of welcome proof of life.

I began to regret my use of the lizard as a measure of human intelligence. I am sure that the irrational fears of most humans are non-existent to the lizards that would calmly swim through the quiet pool, prowling for prey. I wondered about the lizard's lack of insecurity in contrast with the vanity that plagues the human race. As it passed a turtle with its neck craned out of the water like a tall man seeking vision in a crowd, it gave the turtle a kind of nod as if they were friends. As it passed, it ducked its head seemingly in deference to me; deference to me in my human mind or to me, the mindless human who stands still while observing the pond. The loud splash that accompanied the lizard's entrance to my scenario has calmed the pool perceptively. Or could he have filled it with fear intentionally? Maybe the hunting beast senses the sweat of the fish that fear it. The fish swim calmly as they know that their fear gives them away. The monitor reappears in the same place where it started. I have decided that its sex doesn't matter as the geckos cry "uh oh" to those beings who have yet to sense the submerged presence of pre history's contribution to the reed lined pond. The realization that it lies no further from the great city of Ha Noi has yet to come to its inhabitants any more than the realization that humans have of their resistance to truth. Call it evolution or God given, thought processes are retarded by learning, not by genetic defects at birth.

The same education process that makes wild animals dependent on human care takers require rehabilitation before they can be returned to the wild steals the analytical ability from humans that would otherwise make them recognize that the production of their own destruction is counterproductive to sustaining their existence. I sincerely think this as I fabricate the next lie that I will tell the woman who has come to my attention as she now stands in front of me, gazing into my eyes as my thoughts follow yet another lizard across the water. A horrible liar I am. I sincerely believe this.

Welcome to Laos

(How to meet lovely women. Take Two)

There was a time in my life when flying was simply a terror for me. Nothing in the anticipation of the great destination at which I would be arriving could change that. My first real plane flight was for a high school football trip. The flight was from my hometown in Great Falls, Montana to Boise, Idaho. I had been excited to have been chosen to go as I was a scrub, and the coaches most likely chose me over a more worthy player as a kind of sympathy manoeuvre. Despite not even being second string at any particular position, I was in my last year of high school, and I was probably the only senior who would not have gone had they chosen to leave me at home. I suppose I boarded the plane with the same teenage bravado of my teammates but once the plane started to taxi, I became uncomfortable and the moment it left the ground, I wanted the hell out! I have since often imagined that if planes had exit doors and there were no safety regulations, how people would look cartwheeling down the runway after tossing themselves out of the plane as it left the safety of Mother Earth. By choice, by the way... by choice.

The terror of flight has long been in my past, but I have often sensed the fear of another, particularly when flying in developing countries where there are always first-time passengers and the fear in the cabin is almost palpable as it permeates the air. Frightened faces with forced smiles cannot hide the horror felt by those to whom every sensation is new and even a slight glance out of one of the windows is a picture of the reality they are living, with just a blank curtain of air separating them from their current position and a fiery crash on the ground.

My first flight would turn out quite to be somewhat of a pleasure. Despite the fact that I was truly terrified during most of the journey, the one and only flight attendant, a very attractive brunette who looked about the same age as me and my teammates, took it upon herself to console me throughout the trip, sometimes holding my hand which convinced me for future reference that the aisle seat was the seat for me. I remember other players feigning fear and holding their hands out but… she stuck with me. And this became kind of a pattern for my future travel. I would either meet an attractive woman in the waiting area for a flight or at some point during a flight. For much of my flying life though, this did not really quell my fears, and being on the verge of a scream of terror was not the best mode in which to make a good first impression, but the "luck" of consistently meeting attractive women did make me feel a whole lot better about flying.

I suppose it had something to do with odds, or maybe the fact that I was losing some of the cuteness of my youth, but this "luck" was happening less and less as the years flew by and air travel became a regular activity in my life. I had moved from Merced, California to Nice, France and it was rare that a month would go by when I was not on a plane at least once or twice. Flying was no longer a terror or even a thrill. I suppose there had been a certain attractivity communicated by my vulnerability. And the intensity of this that I had been exhibiting as a nervous traveller was replaced with a kind of cranky, pissed off attitude that one attains when confronted by a routine or unwelcome task.

I had become a fan of the turbulence that had petrified me as a novice passenger and the rougher the flight, the more I enjoyed it. And, by no coincidence, I preferred riding in the small twin engine propeller planes that are sometimes used on short regional hops. I have been a lifelong motorcyclist and to me the feeling of the airplane bouncing around in the clouds is similar to that of a dirt bike going over a set of whoop de doos. I had grown up on dirt bikes and I remember another terror, my first ride on a real powerful street bike which, on a smooth surface, felt as though I was riding on a sheet of ice. This was similar to how I felt in a jumbo jet floating smoothly across the sky. I was definitely more comfortable being tossed to and fro.

I had an opportunity of employment at an international school in Vietnam and I took it. The flight there was uneventful, and I recall that when we were approaching Ha Noi, I really felt like I was going home. As I looked down at the landscape, the Red River snaked its way through the green rice fields that looked a bit like the wheat farms that line the Missouri River near my home. I had already conquered my fear of flying pretty much and I was determined to see all of Southeast Asia during my tenure there, so I began thinking of places and planning.

The airline magazine that I was aggressively scan reading was a great source of ideas. I delved into the section in Laos, then Cambodia. I had been on a brief journey to Phuket, Thailand while I was working in South Korea, but Bangkok still held my attention, and I slowed my reading while I was in that section to catch more detail. I hardly noticed that we had landed.

Not so long after I arrived, as I was settling into my new life, I was invited to attend a lacquer painting class. I was soon a regular at the Fine Arts University. I kept overhearing some of the other expat students talk about Laos, a magical place, and I decided I would travel there as soon as I could.

Going to Vientiane was not complicated but going there on Air Laos was quite expensive compared to flights to other sites in SE Asia. This did not deter me as I had decided it would be a great inspiration for a masterpiece that was undoubtedly in the works.

Check in was easy, it seemed we would be having a quite a few empty seats, but I realized the estimation was entirely incorrect when the bus from the terminal arrived at the plane. I was thrilled that it was a twin-engine turbo prop much like the one on which I recently ridden in a flight from Spokane to Great Falls. I harkened back to memory of my first flight so many years before. And, sure enough, the seat lottery had been good to me, and I was seated next to a prim sophisticated woman who seemed just as enthusiastic as I was about her seat mate.

We barely introduced ourselves when we were already sharing our plans on what we were going to be doing in Laos and, coincidentally, they were almost identical: Open! According to our conversation neither of us had any particular plan though I suspected she was the type that had everything worked out down to the minute. Perhaps she suspected me of the same. Any suggestion made became an item on our now shared agenda and we were both champing at the bit to get things started!

I noticed that she kept glancing back to look through the tiny space between our seats in what seemed a pretext to close the distance between our beaming faces to bring our lips together. At the same time, I could feel an ominous presence.

The woman behind was obviously eavesdropping and making her presence known by pressing her face against the back of the seat of the woman next to me and breathing heavily through the space between them.

The plane banked sharply to the left and, I heard a loud scream. I could not believe I had screamed and so loudly. The woman behind us apologised.

I cooly said "no problem" though I wanted to say thank you for screaming for me. She was right in apologising though. I don't think she was apologising for the scream; I don't even think it was meant out of her fear of the plane going down but rather out of the success that I was having with the lady next to me. This must have been horrifying to her. I have never really taken the time to wonder about this, but it seems almost a requirement for folks of a certain age to begin to believe that everyone's business is their own, except for maybe their own. There was no mirror on the back of the seat, but I suppose if there was, I could have seen that my eyelashes were twisted into eyebrows and my eyes were bulging out! I know this because my seat mate was in a similar state. The terror brought on by her scream proved to be an amazingly effective cockblock. The lady and I were silent throughout the twenty or so minutes which remained in the flight. The uncomfortable silence made it seem like hours. I don't think the landing came quickly enough for either of us and my fair lady was barely a memory a few hours later when I would have my first bout with Laotian food and the intensity of its midday sun. As I passed one of the local weed salesmen, I found his offer peculiar as I was already hallucinating from the incredible sting I had inflicted on myself. Between the heat of the chillies, I had no business eating and the sauna-esque humidity that was sucking the moisture out of my innards and pouring it all over my epidermis, I had no need whatsoever for any other foreign substance. It occurred to me that it could be worse. I could be suffering in the company of the lady, a kind of recurrence of what had occurred on the plane. I convinced myself that I was better off alone. I thought back to some of the wisdom that my mother had shared with me when I was a child. I was on time, and I had enough money to pay so... Oh yeah... Can't win for losin', my other talent.

The Victim

I have changed my choice of prepositions. I no longer say, "What happened TO me?" I say, "What happened with me?". Life can be cruel and people crueller. Misery may love company but the miserable love cruelty. Anytime that I have sought to be consoled, that "Shoulder to cry on" has become nothing more than a tool with which one pries open my saddest of thoughts, spills them out in front of me and gives each one a squeeze until they see which ones bring the most genuine grimace to my face and then wrinkle those up and put them in their pockets for future use. This used to be surprising to me. It never should have been. It is a rare human who truly knows compassion; this is most likely why most folks love pets.

I used to be fond of this line from the poem *Prospice* by Robert Browning "For sudden, the worst turns the best to the brave". The context in which I first heard this was on a kind of docudrama about the explorer Ernest Shackleton who I had not heard of before I watched the show. I had not heard of Robert Browning either. I eventually made my way to a library where I found a collection of his poetry and found "*Prospice.*" I was a disillusioned that it was about surviving the death of a beloved wife rather than some sort of epic quest. I tried to remember a death that had affected me.

My father died when I was sixteen. It was not such a trauma as one might imagine; it was just something that happened, and I rarely recall much about it. It is only when strangers ask, and I guess family is something that is eventually discussed when strangers meet. This seemed to happen a lot after I moved to California which made sense as I was a stranger to everyone there. Whenever someone would ask me what my father did, I would want to say, "He lies in the ground in a hole." But I thought this seemed callous and might make the asker believe that I was fishing for sympathy by pretending not to care. And I wasn't sure that I did. There are some things that just happen in life. Misfortune and tragedy are relative, one might even say they are relatives.

I am not sure that hard liquor is supposed to be affected negatively with age but the rum I was drinking tasted absolutely stale. The bite of the alcohol was gone. There was a sugary remnant of what was left of the cane that had given its life for the beverage lining the threads on the bottle which held the cap on. I poured what I guessed to be one more finger into the glass, measured vertically, and went on with my task of getting intoxicated.

Sadly, I could not conjure up one of those romantic images that are normally associated with the consumption of alcohol. I wanted a beach scene, but I must have dreamed it wrong because I was on a bench, a park bench and the fumes from the gardener's fuel container that he had purposefully laid next to me seemed fragrant compared to the elixir that was doing its best to melt its way through its prison in the plastic cup from which I was drinking it. I liberated a bit, making it captain of my soul.

I wasn't sure which was more flammable, the petrol or my breath but I figured I had better move on before I made another attempt at giving flame to my cigarette. If you play with matches, you will get burned goes the saying. I, on the other hand, would go up in flames. The box of matches I had, were from the same café where I had bought the rum and were in similar condition to that rum. I thought I should spark away for a bit to see if I could get the gardener to take heed and remove the rusty gas can he had placed next to me, but I thought he might get creative and strike it against the concrete a few times and demonstrate that he too could produce a spark.

The thought of the two of us standing there burning to death chuckling away at what we had done to one another might have made a good scene in some commercial but not for rum, so I got up and started heading back to the tiny two storied office space that I was using as a studio. I wondered if I would end up sleeping on the yoga mat that I had on the first floor. The ladder like staircase that led to the second floor was somewhat imposing even when I was sober and nearly impossible when I was adrift in the drunken world.

Belching came easy I thought as I burped my way down the empty sidewalk. It was right around noon and no one with any sense was out walking. They were all escaping the blazing rays of the sun, tucked into their lunches in the numerous cafés and restaurants which line the concrete shores of the artificial lakes which dot this wetland of a city.

"That was a loud one." I said to myself but aloud and my audience chuckled.

"It certainly was." she said as I rounded the corner.

And here she was staring me straight in the face. "Didn't I have a hundred or so meters to go? Wasn't she supposed to be waiting at the studio? Wait! Was it really Wednesday?

I fondled myself heartily in an attempt at my phone. My grip on the bottle was tight, so were my pants. I could not get my right pocket to release my left hand which I knew not how I got it into in the first place.

Failure knows no bounds. I have never been good with planners, but it is rare that I miss an appointment. The captain of my soul had called much too early that morning. I had made the appointment at 11 so I could stick to my 12 o'clock rule. It is a good rule. And it was with this discipline that I would find my success.

Watching her elegance pour into the rear seat of the cream-coloured Bentley as her driver gracefully closed the curtain on our final act while gifting me with a sneer, I shuddered at the thought that this could well have been the commercial I had dreamed... and it would remain a dream.

I was no longer staggering. Dignity held my head high. There is dignity in being a failed artist. I am uncertain how true the successful can remain to their craft.

I told this story to an acquaintance one day. I might have changed one detail or another, but the result was the same. "It serves you right." He said when I mentioned that earlier she had not only agreed on a dozen paintings but also my high market price. "A collector" he said, "doesn't buy one painting at a time, they buy collections." Oddly enough, I had told him this during my story but like most of the artist elements in the story, he took ownership of this too.

"Yes! As I said and I think she could have given me a second chance." I grovelled.

"Why would she? People like you are a dime a dozen.", He said obviously avoiding the word artist and emphasising his use of dozen to steal the effect of the actual numerical value of the word. His attitude caught me as quite cavalier for a guy who had, in an accident of honesty, one time admitted that he hadn't sold a dozen pieces in his life.

He continued as though he was being generous. After all, wasn't he "giving" advice to me? The shoulder on which I had come to cry had once again turned frigid. Shoulders are not meant for crying on. They are for hanging jackets.

I noted mentally that it was his round about ten rounds ago. Phonies are like that. The exaggeration of their self-importance makes them immune to decorum as well as standards. The world is their oyster; it would be absurd for them to have to pay for anything. He was always very conscientious about offering to cooperate whenever a wealthy guy we hung out with was paying but he had no such concern for my pocketbook. It was like he was trying to milk me dry. He used the same method for sucking the life out of my feelings. He is not alone. I wondered if this is why I create, to breathe meaning into the soulless existence into which life is hammered. In that, I cannot fail... I do not fail.

Scandal

I usually travel with some sort of sketch pad about the size of a pocketbook, a pad of water colour paper of a similar size, a couple of pencils and pens and some sort of compact watercolour pack and a brush or two. My favourite watercolour pack is just a little larger than the wallet in which I carry my business cards. It has ten colours, including white and black, and a small square water reservoir for mixing. The brush that came with it is designed like a pen. It has screw tops at both ends, one to protect the brush and one cap for the tiny water compartment that holds just enough water to fill the reservoir about half full. I favour this kit over another one that I have which has five discs which screw together. It holds a total of thirty colours, but the tiny box is easier to conceal and the random curious are much more hesitant to pick up the little box than one of the discs.

While this may not be true, I tend to believe that I get what I consider an excess of attention in every country that I travel, and I definitely don't travel to get attention. I don't think I ever have. Before you go saying nobody does, hold onto that particular horse and think social media. It is a rare traveller who isn't posting as they go and so very "unrare" indeed that it seems that the only reason the person actually travels is to get attention. And, as you are reigning in that horse go back to the previous century (BSM Before social media) and even without social media, folks were physically posting cards, from all over the place! I can recall folks in airports busily filling out post card after post card almost like they were filling in so many spaces on a job application so that they could rush them over to the airport post office to get them stamped in the country they were leaving so that they wouldn't have to throw them away. How embarrassing could that to be to post them after they had left the post cards' country of origin or even returned to their home country before posting them? In the ASM world, that would seem the equivalent to the scammers who use software to add themselves into places they have never been and will never be.

This is not to say that I am not guilty of all of the above, save the photoshop scam though this is due more to lack of technical skill than to honesty, but I usually end up wanting to paint and write while traveling and I like to avoid getting attention when I am creating. Whether it is writing or painting, I have never been one of the folks who go to a café or park with some ostentatious display of artistry in hopes that someone will come and have an engaging chat. When I lived in my wonderful neighbour-hood in La Jolla, back in the late eighties, it would be rare that I would find myself without a book and likely that I would head straight for the local bookshop if I did. Of course, we were not yet plagued with mobile phones and social media, so it was a much different game, but I was never self-conscious about reading and I was almost never annoyed when someone asked what I was reading. But, when it comes to creating, I prefer to do this in the privacy of some self-designed prison cell, which others might call a studio, or out in the countryside far away from inquiring eyes.

After having abandoned the beach areas just south of Bar-celona due to the holiday traffic, I was taking a circuitous route to Bilbao, not by design but rather lack of a GPS signal and poor planning beforehand. I had rented a well-used Seat Leon which would cruise comfortably at 140 km/h but commence to float around 150, the way old American luxury cars do. Jetlag was getting the best of me and this gentle floating was putting me to sleep.

Fortunately, the motorway was nearly empty as I slowed to a stop before making the decision to take the exit I had been rolling up to. There was a sign for a ski area which was obviously closed as it was July, but I reckoned that it might have a hotel, probably pricey but I had little choice as I had no idea where I was. As I reached the top of the off ramp, I noted that there was a hotel on the other side of the motorway, and I decided that left was preferable to right. I was still reeling from my panic state. I was thinking how lucky I was to have caught myself closing my eyes, a few more seconds could have put me off the road. The Seat drifted along on the overpass as my muddled mind coasted in its state of indecision.

The hotel sign that I had seen led to an abandoned property, another victim of scammers in the fake financial economy that has perverted the world. I decided that I would just sleep in the car. About a hundred meters away, I saw a man who appeared to be beckoning me, and I idled up to him, mind in neutral, car barely moving. I slammed on the brakes which raised a bit of the dry dusty surface of the road.

"Está cerrado... Hay otra para allí." He said as he pointed at a place down the road. It was about thirty seconds away, I expected it to be a tourist trap so when I arrived, I contemplated returning to the parking lot of the abandoned place to catch a nap in the car but a few moments without the air conditioning convinced me that was a bad idea. It was sweltering. I opened the rear compartment. I touched the sweating five litre bottle of water which was nearly ice cold when I had bought it about an hour earlier. It was pretty damn hot, and I wondered how much hotter the trunk would have been without it absorbing some of the heat. Looking out into the distance, I could see heat waves rising from the road. I took a bag from the trunk and headed to the front desk prepared to pay whatever and expecting the worst.

"Vente euro." The man at the desk said as he perused the old worn registration book. It looked like a prop from a Western film, its black cover was worn to grey around its edges.

I pulled out my wallet to pay.

"Paga despues." He continued as he forced the iron key into my palm. Though the reception area was not air conditioned, it was so much cooler than the outdoors that it seemed almost frigid. I shivered but felt warm. I was very thankful that I had chosen to rent a car rather than a camper van as I had originally planned. It would have been a virtual oven without the air conditioning running all night.

I returned my wallet to my pocket and started up the stairs head nodding back and forth. I was fairly certain that I would be unconscious before I got to the top of the stairs but when I reached the upper floor, I caught a bit of a second wind. The thought of a great night's sleep had me desirous of a meal and a good bottle of wine. As I opened the curtain covering the room's only window, the sun told me that dusk was still at least an hour away. I have been there before on many of my travels, too early to bed and then an early AM wake up to hours of lonely darkness with an empty stomach and a mind full of regret. I do not learn lessons but live them. On occasion I live them well.

Dinner was phenomenal. It was a set menu with an amazingly refreshing gazpacho, a perfectly cooked, incredibly tender *secreto iberico* and a gorgeous flan for dessert. The highlight of the meal was the wine though. A wonderful bottle of rioja, for about 8 euro, had me reeling with pleasure. I took it outside to finish with a couple of cigarettes and as the heat began to subside, I took inventory of the surroundings. The last waves of the heat of the day gave the horizon a surrealistic effect, not unlike those in the works of Dali. I knew then that I would not be leaving for at least another day.

I was a bit surprised to find the dining room nearly packed in the morning. There were a few folks in there the night before, but I had imagined that the place would be pretty empty judging from the desolation of the area.

The *cantinero* made an espresso and mentioned that since I skipped it last night, it was included with the dinner from the night before. His gruff manner that undoubtedly had its origins in a rough life in a tough place belied his genuine kindness and sense of hospitality. As I took my leave from the polished wooden bar, he asked if I would be checking out. I said no and smiled. He opened the relic that they used for their accounting and made a mark.

The sun was blazing, and I noticed there was a bar across the road. The road had served as a highway before the motorway was built and it was still the preferred connection for the nearby villages. I couldn't resist. There is something about quaint that draws me like a magnet; between the archaic design of the building itself and the setting in the one horse, end of the world town that I was in, the thought of having a wake up shot of some other worldly local liquor in a second hit of caffeine assured me that I was in a very good place to create something special.

I whisked away with my tiny brush as I dipped it again and again into the water that seemed to be evaporating before my very eyes, the dry air of the day was sucking the moisture off the brush as quickly as I could apply it. The cakes of paint were baking hot, and I imagined the bubbles created by mixing the water with the paint were actually being the result of the boiling hot temperature of the clear morning.

I love the sky on a day like this. It is so much easier to get right. An uninterrupted blue layered beautifully from the highest point to the horizon is truly something to behold. The church was perfectly lighted by the sun as it was still early, about 9 AM, and the direct rays highlighted details with barely any shadow.

I looked around suspiciously as it seemed too good to be true. Was I really going to do this? I knew twenty minutes of focus was enough as I had only to fill a very small pad of watercolour paper. After about twenty minutes, I noticed there were people milling about. I took my leave.

Though I have never framed the piece; I love it. I seem to come across it randomly, whenever I need a reason to carry on. Within the magical experience that I had creating it, I recognized that my failure to give up on love is what drives me to create.

The Church, Spain *(2019) Watercolor on Art Paper*

The Lottery

I had rented a motorcycle in Lisbon. It was my first journey to Portugal, and it would be my first journey on a rented motorcycle. The rental service specialized in BMW adventure bikes starting at 700ccs and went all the way to the 1200 GS. My choice of the 800 model had as much to do with my inseam as anything else. Even with the lowering adjustment, I was not confident that I could handle one of the larger, heavier models with confidence in the city traffic in which I would inevitably find myself. I was also mindful that at 57 years old, the gymnastics I would have to perform to mount a bike with full bags every time I stopped was imposing, even with the smaller 800. I had planned on doing as much off-roading as possible and the thought of lifting the GS 1200 up after a spill would certainly have me being cautious and caution has a way of killing confidence. If I have learned anything about riding motorcycles in my forty plus years of experience, it is that riding is all about confidence. If one does not have it, they should not be riding. And arrogance is not the same as confidence. I have met many riders in my travels that would have been much better off on a small displacement model or a bus. The fact that they were surviving their journeys was certainly as much due to dumb luck as anything else. Their enjoyment came from a beginner's sense of thrill, and the chest pounding bullshit sessions that the overly challenging hours spent on their oversized steeds produced for them. The bravado they displayed as they recounted the events of their days often had me wondering how they arrived at the same place as me. Their onerous encounters with the travails of the trail made my travels along the same roads seem petty and pathetic by comparison. The fact that I made much better time on a much smaller bike somehow made me a novice by their standards.

As I waited for one agent to finish my check out, I couldn't help but overhear the advice of the other agent who was expressing his concerns to another renter and his passenger. It seems the lessor had decided that he could "handle" a bike of any displacement due to his weight while the lessee had decided that his girth might be the final factor in bringing the big bike to the ground, rubber side up so to speak. The would-be passenger meekly supported her partner though her fear seemed to be growing by the moment. I was relieved to get out of the place as she seemed to be hoping for intervention as she cocked her head in my direction several times and appeared to be searching my soul with her pleading eyes. There is no cure for stupidity though; the fact that most of us survive it means it is not the death sentence that evolution should dictate.

In my case, my stupidity would have me buzzing along at high rpms on the motorways on the "economical" smaller ccs model for hours at a time. My original plan had me cutting across the countryside along country roads that would have made the smaller model the best choice, but this was not to be. If I would have stayed that course, I would have arrived at my eventual destination, Nice, France, in weeks if not months and I had but one week. Better planning and a few more bucks would have been well spent so that I could have reduced my saddle time in a much more comfortable saddle! I think the vibration alone took a couple of years off my life. Born to lose is a popular expression bad ass bikers in the states wear on patches on their jackets or vest. I felt a born loser as my ass was definitely bad at the end of each day.

Regardless of my state at the end of any motorcycling day, I am always ready to go the next morning, sometimes too ready. I have ridden into awful weather, suffered heat stroke, nearly froze to death and had some genuinely horrible experiences which could have been easily avoided by a few hours wait or simply staying in one place another day. But wherever I wake up, I am gripped with the desire to move.

The angry sun that had been baking me dry on the plains east of Madrid was replaced by a mean and deceitful shower in Barcelona. The rain burst from the clouds in buckets, then, like an orchestral piece that catches the audience off guard during a pause, the thunder would be suddenly clapping despite a halt in the rain. Then, the rain would recommence with a ferocity that no composer could hope to recreate. I would start out of the city during one of the short dry spells only to be met by a torrent the moment I would get back on the motorway. This would last about a half hour or so. I would decide to exit, and the skies would clear by the time I was near the city. I had been through several cycles of the wet and dry before I decided to call it a day. The filth that flowed from the gutters in Barcelona added a stench to my outerwear that had me in the shower before I took them off. They were already completely saturated, so it seemed the thing to do. A new set of clothes and a couple of beers later, I was good as new.

Temptation to stay in Barcelona was great. Though I have spent little time there, it is one of my favourite cities in the world. It was not so much that the road was calling that I left there, though I was on a schedule, it was the

115

thought of riding around the city among the frenetic Spanish drivers that got me on my way.

Barcelona to Nice was uneventful though I took an extra day to stop and get horribly drunk in Cannes with a former student and her husband who happened to be there. I stayed with them after our night out. My hosts had already left the tiny Airbnb before I woke. I don't understand the allure of Airbnb; waking up in some stranger's home, particularly after a night out is only a slight improvement over waking up on the street. I scraped the hell out of the bike's side cases while negotiating my way out of the narrow stone lined passage that led to the street. I had brought them in to keep them from getting stolen. I reflected on the intelligence of that seeing that I supposed that I would have to pay for the scrapes when I brought the bike back.

Cannes to Nice was painless but having not been to Nice for so many years, it became the land of confusion. The motorway that rings the city was not there so many years ago and I was uncertain about the exits. I thought that the GPS on my Samsung was not functioning correctly as it was guiding me in the opposite direction of my instincts. I was unconcerned by this initially as I do know the city quite well but there were so many changes! I did not realize that my friend had moved until I pulled up to what used to be his gate and recognized that I had programmed the address correctly, the GPS was fine and even my inner directional signal was functioning. He had moved!

Pierre's new address was actually familiar to me as when I first visited him so many years ago, I lived very near there. Upon arrival I was proclaimed a proper jerk and given a lecture as, for some reason, an email was misunderstood, and they had been expecting me since the day before. Sadly, I have to say that this is not nearly the first time that this has happened with them. I have a history of this in relation to them and it was merely a continuation.

To say my stay was refreshing is an understatement as Pierre and his wife have always been a pinnacle of hospitality for me and this visit was no different. I was suddenly happy to be on a sort of schedule as I tore myself away after a couple of days and headed back towards Spain.

The World Cup was on, and France was doing quite well. I stopped in Toulouse near a McDonalds just in time to see an AIR BUS JUMBO fly over at low altitude. It was a magnificent site. It was so huge that it almost appeared stationary as it made its way towards its landing space.

When I arrived in Salamanca a couple of days later, I bought a lottery ticket, not necessarily with the idea of winning but rather with the idea that I was not giving up on becoming rich. Whether it came by luck or hard work, I would continue to grind away. Suicide lives not in me.

There was a fellow who declared himself my kindred spirit. I remember being aghast and thinking on what planet. But later I found myself gravitating towards him. Within the ugliness of jealousy and envy are found admiration. Everyone wants to be admired. The jealous and envious affirm our very selves.

Paris

Paris initiates no dramas. They are begun elsewhere.
Henry Miller; from the *Tropic of Cancer*.

The story was supposed to be about rum, but it ended up being about artists. I don't recall how I learned of La Rhumerie on St. Germaine in Paris but it was a bit before the internet went public so it must have been something like Guide Routier or word of mouth. But I was destined for the place nonetheless. I did quite a bit of writing at the time, though I didn't make the drama out of it that many of the artsy crowd that I met in France did. Still, I had my moments. I did not begrudge the other pretenders theirs. But...

I had come to Paris with a couple, Alain and Elise. We had driven up from somewhere in the south near Antibes. I was loaned to them by a friend in Nice. I can't recall why I was welcome, but I suppose it was to defray the costs of tolls and fuel. The friend who loaned me to them stressed that I should not cooperate in the costs as they would be paying them regardless, and my presence in the car was, if anything, a bonus as they could practice speaking English and it would keep them focused on something besides each other which would in turn keep them from boring each other or arguing. He didn't explain the boring and arguing part, but he did mention the English and I didn't feel too guilty when they turned back and smiled at me after every fill up and toll.

I actually had plenty of cash and it was burning holes in my pockets as cash always did whenever I had a bit after the frequent bouts of broke-assedness that I survived while struggling to find my way in Nice. I reached into those pockets on more than one occasion and displayed this cash to Alain, the male half of the couple. He declined my offers though I suppose he would have taken some of the cash if I had actually handed it to him. There was no tension though, that would be reserved for the return trip when their expectations seemed to rise to the same level that the amount of cash that I was carrying had dropped; I have often noted that there is an inverse relationship that folks with cash have with cash. They are willing to pay for anything someone they are hosting can afford but extremely unwilling to support that which that same person cannot. And their generosity knows no bounds when the person has more than they do!

Our arrival in Paris was glorious. They had a time share that was on the top floor of a twelve-story building. The carpet there was a red that need not be described as anything other than red. It flowed through the building like an introduction to the Cannes Film Festival and I remember thinking that and wondering what the hell they would do for a special event there. And that was most probably the beginning of the end.

I am cynical by nature, and we are, as Emerson put it, what we think about all day long. Alain had brought his mountain bike with him. He competed in amateur events and was training for one. I recall wondering where he was going to ride in Paris, but it is a big city and I had supposed that this question would be nothing other than a display of my ignorance of this.

I was also very active on a mountain bike though I never competed. I rode mostly in the hills that surround Nice and I was very fit to say the least. I am short, about 170 cm, and Alain is not, he is about 195 cm and though his bike was about as light as a couple of baguettes, it was enormous. It had to have been at least 20 cm taller than mine with the seat at its lowest, and it could well have been 40 cm longer.

The interior of the elevator was quite elegant, but it had no space for this monster. If I had waited, I am sure the concierge would have taken it up in a service elevator that they hid somewhere else in the building. But... I decided right then and there that there would be none of that sophistication. (It was actually my ignorance of the fact that a service elevator would be required to bring larger objects like anything as uncommon as the furniture with which each and every apartment was filled but that might make me look the fool and I will end up the hero in this story so I will not admit to that.)

Though not really a cowboy from Montana, I am from Montana and a cowboy I was purported to be. "They ain't wrong they are just different,' as the song says and after deciding that riding the towering steed up the stairs could have been impressive, I recognized that it could also end up horribly for all involved, especially my gonads.

So, I threw the massive but nearly weightless machine onto my shoulder and commenced to sprint up the stairs. As mentioned above, I was in fabulous physical condition. I arrived at the twelfth-floor penthouse about 30 seconds before the elevator. I credit this to speed, but it was probably the paralysis of shock in which I had left the concierge and his passengers. I am sure a French thesaurus contains most of the words in that language for idiot, but it would not surprise me if, before their ascent, the trio had emptied out all of the synonyms for "Idiot" that even the best French thesaurus could contain and invented a few of their own. This was most likely the cause of their delay.

The excessive level of enthusiasm with which the couple greeted me when the elevator arrived was matched by the disgust on the visage of the concierge and I decided that his face was the true measure of the situation, and it would be best to sprint my way back down and flee before they could invite me in. I had but a small bag, which they had so kindly loaded in the elevator for me and the mind reading concierge had made the same sense of the situation that I had, and he held it out like a hand-off from a quarterback in American football. I am not unfamiliar with the game or embarrassment, and I took the hand-off without hesitation and shouted a promise to be back at our appointed time as they shouted their reconfirmation of it.

I was out on the street before I realized that I had little or no idea where Patrick, the guy with who I would be staying lived much less La Rhumerie for that matter. I had called Patrick from a gas station about an hour earlier and given him the logistics, including our ETA, but I had a sudden loss of confidence as I watched the rush hour traffic flash by.

I hardly had a moment to breathe before I felt a hearty slap on my back and was embraced by Patrick. He popped a motorcycle helmet on my head. Before I realized what was happening, I was being given a tour of Paris on the back of his BMW at speeds which I suppose I could politely say made me uncomfortable or more correctly had me wondering whether or not I would have shit in my pants when they scraped me off the road after our inevitable accident.

If you are lucky enough to have lived in Paris as a young man, then wherever you go for the rest of your life, it stays with you, for Paris is a moveable feast.

Ernest Hemingway.

When one is traveling at an accelerated pace, one feels alive. This is living. Nothing makes one feel so alive as the feeling of being close to death.

Thankfully, Patrick shut off the gas and flipped up the shield of his helmet whenever he wanted to point out something. We coasted around the Arc de Triomphe and I remember feeling a bit triumphant to still be alive.

Patrick's apartment was typical of Paris, or so he told me. The living room was quite spacious, and it shared its spaciousness with an antique looking eight seat dining room table. The bathroom and toilet were separate and the one bedroom, which he shared with his wife, was apparently fairly roomy as well but he did not show it to me. The kitchen was tiny to say the least. I was a bit surprised as the kitchen in my tiny apartment in Nice seemed gigantic by comparison.

I met Patrick in Nice where he was doing some sort of work, I never asked about it. He was taking English classes from me, and he was there alone so we ended up going to dinner and hanging out a bit. His wife was at work when we arrived at their apartment. Patrick assured me that she was thrilled to be meeting me. He cautioned me that her English wasn't as good as his and I found this odd because he and I spoke French when we went out together and even during lessons. It was a sign of things to come.

One who is not French should decline any invitation to cook for the French. French cooking techniques do not translate any better than their humor and any attempt at food preparation by a non-French is almost always met with disdain if not disgust.

Simple things which produce smoke like searing a steak properly can set off a fire alarm, not any battery powered unit but rather the French for whom you are cooking. And as the alarm was sounding directly in my ear, I wondered if Patrick regretted my presence in his apartment if not on the planet.

No one feels as unwelcome as a welcome guest in a French house. I am sure there were those who faced the guillotine with a higher comfort level.

The blue cheese that was supposed to be in the sauce for the parboiled meat would have taken about 30 minutes if not hours to melt at the temperature they expected me to cook it and there was no hope in the cream ever coming to a boil, so I left the cream in the container and put slices of blue cheese on the plates. The myth that all of the French appreciate food and wine is not true. I would have to say that most of the French people that I know are no more connoisseurs of fine food and wine than your average middle class American. I have seen the sacred foie gras go to waste when served at holiday meals and I have experienced some awful meals at the houses of folks who believed in their own cooking, apparently due to the myth. I have also noticed that the whining that some do at the table is more a result of their desire to seem sophisticated than their actual knowledge of the quality of the food or wine.

My cooking was more than satisfactory as it gave them something to bitch about and was proof that one must be French to cook. One has never truly experienced a true love of food until one sits through three courses of pissing and moaning about overdressed salad, a perfectly cooked steak that could have been edible if it had a decent sauce, and under-cooked pasta which, if my understanding was correct, should have been boiled with the water from cold to boiling much like the proverbial frog in the frog boiling myth which is no more true than the one about French people appreciating good food. Perhaps if I had not unwrapped it and just put it close enough to the heat, it would have steamed to perfection right there in the plastic wrapper. That way we could have kept the steam from the boiling water in the pot from drawing the beads of sweat from the three of us who, for no good reason, were huddled in the kitchen over the two-burner stove like we were in the Antarctic struggling to survive in sub-zero temperatures. Rest assured, there was no water harmed in the making of that pasta. There was talk of fruit for dessert, but there was none to be had so it was decided that the slices of blue cheese on the plate with the steak served double duty. And why not? They were certainly not in the sauce. I have not mentioned wine because there wasn't any. Patrick had said that his wife would pick some up on her way home, but she explained during dinner that wine was something that guests are expected to bring so it had slipped her mind. I wouldn't have taken a coffee had they offered but they didn't, and they retired to their room at about 9 PM with a couple of cups and a steaming stove top espresso maker.

Sleep would not come easy. The couch on which I was exiled was perfectly designed for guests. No guest would wish to survive more than three days sleeping on it. After my first night, I recognized that sleep deprivation is an expectation in Paris, and it is not rest and relaxation that fuels the frenzy of the Parisian but rather the constant infusion of caffeine from the tiny cups of espresso that they slurp down maniacally over the course of a day. This also explains their extraordinary patience and good humour.

Rhumerie

My entrance to the Rhumerie was without event. I was used to putting on airs. In the cafes in my neighborhood in Nice, folks were accustomed to acknowledging me with my notebook in hand, scribbling away. A knowing nod, a polite wave, everyone wants to know a celebrity, even if he is just a writer.

It seemed a busy place despite having many empty seats, the kind of place that draws throngs of tourists only to disappoint them. It had the nervous energy that cafés have around lunch and dinner time and the kind of suspense that landmarks like it create as the possibility of a celebrity dropping by always seems possible.

I imagined the place hadn't changed much since its creation in the nineteen thirties. There are some places that never change, when you see them the first time, it is like déjà vu. It looked like a set from a movie that would be based on the time when it was opened, not long after the Lost Generation had moved on.

I chose my table carefully. The waiter, clad in traditional black and whites, observed but did not intervene. I could imagine that he had seen many great artists in his time, and he certainly wasn't going to interfere with my acclaim by ushering me into some random table in the center of the room like he might some tourist. I saw a middle-aged couple seated at a table in the corner next to the bar. They seemed to beckon me, egging me on in my charade, obviously very experienced observers of the craft.

Settling down at a table with my back to the window, diagonally opposed to the most obvious of my admirers, I felt a bit of relief that I hadn't taken the bait and introduced myself. They could very well have been celebrities themselves. Whenever I see a detective show about someone who passed away "too young", there is always a friend or two who will say that the deceased was the type that would "light up a room". As this is a characteristic that seems to get one murdered, I tend to avoid the thought. There was plenty of light in that room, were I to have collapsed and died right there on the spot, I would have preferred "star power" to describe me and I wasn't about to steal my own thunder by bowing down to a couple of famous big shots.

I thought it the obvious choice. I had a great view of the room. It was the only two top in the row and maybe even the entire restaurant. I am not fond of writing while seated at a bar, I can't imagine any real writer ever being, so that was out. With the window at my back, it was basically the least obtrusive spot where I could place myself. As brazen as I pretend to be, my Montana manners and humility always have me settling in some out of the way space wherever I go, and it was as close to out of the way as one could be in a place like that. Truth be told, our insecurities make most of our decisions. Whether we flow with them or against them, they are the tides which propel us.

The waiter placed the menu carefully in front of me; I appreciate care. I skipped right past the cocktail section which seemed to garner his approval. And there it was, la crème de la crème. I know very little about rum, but I knew that a shot of anything that hit the fifty-dollar mark in that type of institution had to be worth the journey. I ordered. If my memory serves me as well as the waiter did, it was a 1941. I am not sure of the name on the label, but its origin was Caribbean. My timeline might have been off a decade but just the thought of it had me on the crew of a rum runner back in the days of Prohibition.

Rather than nodding his approval, the waiter stuck his nose in the air, the French equivalent, and hurried off to the bar. I imagined the celebrity couple in the opposing corner were nodding, or at least giving their necks a stretch. My humble posture, eyes to the table kept me from bearing witness first hand.

One of my favourite passages in literature comes from Hemingway's *The Old Man and the Sea*. After his fish was finally landed the old man barely gets a moment to reflect and then the sharks come.

They hurriedly bounced in through the door, obviously late for an "important" meeting, an important rant. They nestled into a booth adjacent to the paradise that I had made for myself. By the time a waiter arrived at their table, they were already setting the place ablaze. The cloud from their cigarette smoke would have been welcome if it had a muffling effect on their cackle. I could sense the people watchers alight and I turned my head to see them. Like spectators at a tennis match, their glances went back and forth from me to the booth, booth to me. The tension grew. They were up to four now, huddling together on the benches that had more than enough room, an omen that there were more of them to come. Oh joy...

The final straw was the entrance of their mentor, undoubtedly a visiting professor from one the universities that cater to the silly expat brats who grew up in France and their counterparts from abroad. Nothing says culture like sending your kid off to ruin someone else's.

She began to unwrap herself, not unlike a female version of Kharkov's winter fool. The amount of clothes that she was wearing had me guessing she was Canadian, of a northernmost province. Were she have proclaimed that she had come directly from north of the Arctic Circle, I would not have been surprised. And I definitely would have heard it.

The jabbering that had been nearly tolerable became a raucous roar as her admirers showered her with laughter. As she recounted her tale of Parisian traffic and the woes of privilege, I recognized a story and sure enough, rather than leave that to mystery for the innocent within her shouting range, she blurted it out.

"I have finally found an agent for our play!"

A cheer arose. I wondered why she used "our" in her sentence. It was obviously all about her. She lighted her cigarette as if in celebration and I admired her focus as she maintained a line of vision on her group while she verbally addressed the entirety of the Rhumerie.

She waved off the waiter as an interruption and continued her presentation. He seemed peeved as one would, as the group had ordered three espressos between the five of them and were sipping communally. They were making it obvious that they were in Paris to live the bohemian life of the starving artist and maybe starve a waiter or two in the process. This was confirmed when one of them placed a platinum American Express card on the table. "Leave us alone. We can pay." He shouted to the waiter in English. The quizzical look on the waiter at my table placing the snifter of the sweet elixir in front of me was a call to action.

While her act was reaching a crescendo another player had come onto the scene. The distinct odour of Gitanes Brun had entered my olfactory system. These are cigarettes that should be smoked exclusively near plugged up toilets or the dead, the only things that smell worse.

"Can you cover my drink? "I asked.

The waiter deftly took the coaster on which the snifter set and placed it on the top.

"Do you sell cigars?"

"Plus maintenant. We used to."

"Where is the closest tabac that sells them?"

He gave directions.

Though rush hour Parisians do a kind of walk run, I don't think I have ever seen one at a full sprint. I glided past them with ease on my single-minded quest.

The waiter had prepared for me. He had armed himself with a kind of torch, a bit like a small flamethrower. I put the Churchill to my lips. The flame was impressive. It got the attention of the attention deprived at the booth as well as the smoker on the next table. I looked across the room to the people watchers. Though I sensed no emotion in their eyes, I did detect a hint of glee.

The waiter stood attentively as I fumigated the place. The "how dare you" look on the face of the presenter was replaced with one of concern, second hand smoke from a Cuban can be lethal when used professionally. The smoker, who had taken out a magnetic chess set in my absence was apparently finished with his game. Coins came out and they were gone.

The waiter ceremoniously removed the coaster from the top of the snifter and placed it underneath. I felt a bit of pride. The lavish green porcelain cigar ashtray that he had placed on my table was obviously a homage to our appreciation of the good that is left in life. I asked if he would like to join me in a drink. He declined. I barely acknowledged the faint reverberation of the celebrity couple's clapping hands. But then I gave them a nod. They raised their glasses. I raised mine. We toasted. The place brought out a best in me. It deserved that toast.

Semilla de Amor (2016) Oil on canvas 120 cm x 100 cm
from **The Mind Garden Collection.**

Madrid

They were very different times you know. * I know that can be said about any epoch or decade but I think it was more true in this case. The eighties were unique, but the nineties were idiosyncratic. In the mid-nineties, countries in Europe still had their own currencies but talk of this changing was in the air. The almighty Euro had yet to rear its ugly head and one could still speculate with currencies, not in the way that a Soros or investment thieves and bankers would but in real time in real life situations.

My Air Iberia flight from Nice to Mexico City had a twenty-four-hour layover in Madrid. I chose the flight because of this. I had never been to Spain, and I think I remember it had something to do with a Hemingway piece about drinking twenty-four hours in Madrid, something like that.

I wasn't broke but I was a bit cash strapped in the weeks leading up to the flight. I had been told that Spain was much cheaper than France and I was looking forward to having a twenty-four-hour session regardless of the cost. The franc traded strong against the peseta so I was confident that I could afford it.

A couple of days before I left, the lady who had purchased my ticket paid a last payment on her son's classes. I was supposedly being paid to help him maintain the English level that he had attained as an exchange student in the states in a school in Atlanta, Georgia. In reality, I was playing a kind of big brother role to him and being paid pretty handsomely for it. He was an unruly type who apparently took after his father. Of course, all divorcees say this when their child is a brat. It has nothing to do with them. The divorce didn't either. Not sure who was to blame for her choice of the man in the first place. The kid was nearly eighteen years old. His stepfather was an ex-special forces guy who was a great model of discipline and could have moulded the kid straight into shape but he either didn't want to bother or thought it outside of his role. I have often found folks who use that as an excuse for being irresponsible. It is sometimes odd how disciplines and talents in some fields don't translate at all into others. But this is usually not the fault of the discipline but rather just an excuse not to practice it.

I was more than a little excited about the trip. It would be the first time I had been in Mexico, a country I dearly love, for about five years and the thought of a drink and tapas tour of Madrid had me speculating on an enormous return on my investment. I was certain that the time and money that this journey would be costing would be well spent. In those times, I cared about little other than good times and, as that type of thinking often does, it would end up costing much more than I could have ever imagined. And that is quite another story.

When the plane arrived in the airport in Madrid, I immediately went to a currency counter. I exchanged 1000 francs, which was about two hundred US dollars at the time. I can't remember how many pesetas that bought, but I remember thinking about where best to store the stack of bills. Despite my expectation of being away for at least a month, I had packed lightly and did not have a checked bag. I did however have a bottle of champagne that I was bringing to toast with a friend when I got to Mexico. And this was my introduction to the Spanish.

I was stunned when I realized that the lockers for baggage storage were outside the terminal. I was petrified when I went out into the area and recognized how hot it was. At first, I attributed this to the normal difference between the temperature of air-conditioned air and the lack of it but I wasn't in the place for more than a couple of minutes when I realized that I was in the middle of a desert. It was so hot!

The location of the lockers might have had something to do with the ETA, a Basque separatist political group that conducted military operations and bombings. I suppose a baggage storage area in the middle of a crowded airport would be a tempting target and, in the desert setting, they wouldn't even get credit for blowing up a bunch of luggage in the area that was dedicated to this, it was so hot in the place that anything remotely volatile could have exploded or went up in flames on its own.

I took the bottle of champagne out of the nylon backpack and put the pack in the locker. I am not sure of the thought process, but I remember doing this and putting the bottle on top of the bag. The temperature of the inside of the metal locker was amazing. I am certain that if I would have had something that needed to be baked, it would have been done at the same time that it would have been in a 180-degree oven. I was hesitant to leave the champagne in the locker. The guard was not braving the desert climate, preferring the comfort of the inside a/c so I had no one to consult. I knew it wasn't a great idea to leave the bottle there, but I suspected it had been done before without incident. There were, after all, no warning signs so it was probably just a bit of paranoia. It would certainly cool off when the sun went down.

When I gave the key to the guard in exchange for a ticket, I made a smart-ass remark in my heavily accented Spanish.

"Pretty hot in there. Ever had anything blow up?"

"Like what?"

"Like a bottle of champagne."

"No…never."

"Ok cool, I was worried."

"No hay cuidado." He said, "Don't worry."

I began to worry. There is nothing like attaining a second language in adulthood to bring out one's phobias. "No hay cuidado" was often used in Mexican Spanish as a kind of ominous warning, a premonition, an awkward portent that one should start worrying as something awful was about to happen. No hay cuidado. Don't worry. It is going to happen anyway.

I felt ridiculous suddenly. I thought, "My goodness, I have become paranoid."

He must have heard me chuckle as I was walking away.

"Siempre hay un primero ves." He declared. "There is always a first time. It is what we say in Spain."

I recognized then that the Spanish are mind readers, very profoundly mystical folks.

"Welcome to Spain." I thought, "The land of Cervantes."

*I was advised not to write "you know" by teachers who did not know how to write. I often like to write "you know" just as I like to say it. It is not out of expectation that the listener or reader actually have knowledge of what I am saying or explaining but rather an acknowledgement of my understanding that they are understanding and without need for further explanation. Everyone has a slightly different understanding of anything that is said, you know?

Madrid (Part II)

The shock of the heat returned as I went outside the airport. I met two young Americans by a bus stop. They were recent graduates of some university that I had never heard of. They were "backpacking". I told them we could share a cab, but they were certain that a bus was the way to go. I asked them why and they said that the taxi drivers were swindlers. They had a brand-new Lonely Planet guide out and a note on the bookmark they had stuffed in the pages about transportation, so I had no room to argue. I only had 24 hours so I thought a little swindling might be ok. I had just exchanged francs for pesetas and looking at the bulge in the pocket of my Levi's, I figured I had some room for a pretty good swindle.

I waved down a taxi. The driver asked where I was going and I said, "Madrid!" He seemed to find this comical, and he chuckled as he began mentioning possible destinations in Madrid. He said he was impressed by my sense of humor and my ability to express it in Spanish. I told him that this had been won in many hard-fought verbal battles in Guadalajara, Mexico and I was glad he appreciated it.

He told me that he would be taking me on a tour, which I thought was a great thing. I wasn't concerned about the cost. I had never been to Spain, and I was sure that I would enjoy every twist, turn, and detour that he had on his mind. I told him my objective, the 24-hour drinking bout, and he seemed to agree that it was a capital idea. After taking me past a couple of sites that were closed and plazas that looked like ghost towns, he apologized for the Spanish habit of the Siesta several times and then suddenly stopped the car. He pointed across the street at a very trendy looking bistro.

He said, "This is a tourist bar. You do not belong in such a place, but it is the only place that is open."

He tried to charge me about four dollars, and I remembered that the "backpackers" had told me it would be at least fifty. I told him that I wouldn't be paying him four or ten, he would at least have to take twenty. He hemmed and hawed until I challenged him to meet me for a drink later and I said, "If you can't find me, at least do me the honor of letting me buy you a drink." The cynical might think he was scamming me and wanted more but I am from Montana and my cynicism is reserved for other types. I think he was just a fine guy. I put the money on his dashboard and made my way across the empty street.

I went into the bar and gazed at the jamon hanging from the wooden rafters. There were small cups attached to hams to catch drips of melted fat. The metal the cups were made of was very dull and they seemed a bit out of place above the polished elegance of the bar. I sat down and pulled out the wad of pesetas that I had wondering how many would buy me a beer.

"Una cerveza por favor." I said.

"Una caña." Shouted the bartender.

He explained to me that the shape of the glass was the origin of the term caña and that got me curious as I looked at the black chalkboard drink menu which was hung behind the bar.

Other than the staff, the only soul in the place was seated about four seats down from me and being the ebullient fellow that I can sometimes be, I asked if I could buy him a drink.

He immediately popped off his stool and walked over to the one next to mine. As he mounted it, the stool nearly tipped over and I thought that a drunken tumble off one of the fancy things could send a guy to the hospital.

"Dos Brandies de Jerez" He said, and two half full snifters appeared almost as quickly as the sounds of his words left the air."

"Dos cañas." I said. And the game had begun.

He had an accent, but it was very light and when he first spoke, I thought he was Canadian. He dressed like an American with his bright orange Polo shirt, blue jeans, and Converse tennis shoes. But traveling Canadians often mimic Americans hoping to be mistaken for them so they can tell people that they are mistaken while wishing they were not. I told him that I am from Montana.

"I am from Gloucester." He replied. "I have been working in Madrid for the last nine months."

He moved his stack of pesetas next to mine as if to prove a point and said, "The next ones are on me."

Pride is a silly thing and the fact that my stack was barely half of his made me twice as determined to match him drink for drink.

He continued to give me details about his job and life in Madrid but what I remember most is that he didn't want to take a loss on the exchange to British pounds and he was intent on spending every last peseta before he flew out the next day.

"I'll be damned before I'd buy those money changers any drinks."

I told him of my experience with the guys at the bus stop and he continued the damning as he said, "Well if they show up here, I'll be damned before I'd buy those cheapskates any drinks."

"You talk a bit like an American." I said. "But you don't seem to like them."

"Yeah, well I worked with enough of them."

"Well Montana is in America you know."

"Yeah, but you guys are cowboys, or something aren't you?"

"Oh sure." I said. I pointed down to the beige Italian suede leather shoes that I was wearing. "Boots and all."

I told him my objective and mentioned that it was inspired by Hemingway. It was then that we were officially off to the races.

I began telling him about my tour and he knew some of the places that the taxi driver had mentioned. He said that we would be going to Plaza Mayor and some other local spots. He mentioned that he had spent little time discovering the city while he was working there.

"Gainfully employed I was. I haven't had a proper piss up in ages."

"Now that was English."

"Takes me a few to get me back home."

"I lose this phony French accent after about seven."

"Well, bottoms up then. I am getting sick of it."

I chuckled and recognized I was in for a brutal evening.

We pushed back at the plates of tapas that the bartender pushed on us with every drink that we ordered but ended up eating most of them.

"It's impossible to get properly drunk here... but we're going to try."

I nodded.

The man from Gloucester was referring to the fact that we were eating as we were drinking and that was not a feature of the drinking culture from which either of us had come.

I don't recall leaving the fancy place, my next best memory was the Englishman advising me on how not to get thrown out of the five-star hotel that we ended up not drinking at. We had just gone in to use the restroom. He told me that it was all about confidence. We had walked in as if "we owned the place", his words, and walked about confidently with bladders begging to be emptied. I remember wanting to order a drink to end the charade, but the Englishman figured we were too drunk and after we finally found the loo we were on our way.

Another memory was the two of us at a place that had gigantic snifters. He ordered a bottle of brandy. I can still recall that it was a pricey Gran Reserva. The Englishman made a bit of a squawk about whether it was truly what it was labeled and began damning folks who sold counterfeit goods. I recall asking why we didn't just have a drink at the hotel if he was concerned about the quality. But they had him damned as well, with their damned high prices. But it was just drunken bitching, and he didn't dwell on it. There was no real concern.

The half liter that each of us had in the snifters we swished around did not last long. The Englishman was swirling his snifter carelessly with one hand, me much more carefully with two. There was little finesse in either of our techniques but soon the snifters were empty.

The quick exit is an underused survival skill, seldom exercised by the truly drunk. I was eager to try another bottle, but the Englishman paid quickly and that marked the end of our evening. He summoned a cab and offered to take me to the bus station so that I could make my morning flight. I advised him that I would do well to have a nap at a hotel, but he rejected that idea. If I was conscious when we arrived at the bus station, it was not my own doing. It would not surprise me if I were to discover that he and the driver drug me out of the car and placed me on the bench where I woke up. I remember looking at a clock at some point and thinking that there was a good six or seven hours before the morning bus and finding some relief in this I fell into a deep sleep.

Madrid Part III

I awoke to an image on which I could not focus, it was surreal. A woman… Something out of a dream. I was certain that I was dreaming. Her movements seemed practiced as though she was rehearsing for a dance or a role in a play. Her dress swirled as she made her way towards me. I suppose that I should have been startled but I was still too overcome by alcohol.

She looked like she had been transported from the sixties… maybe early seventies. She was a hippy. She was no clearer than a mirage that I had seen several years before on a motorcycle trip in the intense heat of the Baja desert at a time when hope had given up on me and I had almost given up on it. For some reason, that came to mind. But that had not been a mirage, and neither was she.

My eyes were crusty, and my glasses smeared but I saw that she was wearing layers of clothing. I figured she must have been flying. Some people will do anything to avoid checking a bag.

I began thinking about my baggage and the bottle of champagne. How strong was the muselet? Was it strong enough to sustain the pressure? It must have been weakened by the heat.

The woman's hair had grey streaks, too even to be natural. Her hippy gear was worn and faded. She was but a blur, but she was there. Like a fallen angel that had come to revive the last of her flock, her image brought me to attention. I immediately fell into a comic routine, something that the drunken mind conjures as reason attempts to rise from the depths of what is left in consciousness.

"Are you really there?" I inquired. "Or have I dreamed you?"

She looked at me as she pondered the question.

"My husband was taken." She explained as she pointed to the sky. I had not realized that I was sleeping in the open air, plein aire as the art inclined might say.

"Haight-Ashbury." She declared. It seemed a bit of mind reading but I suppose it was normal to know that I was wondering.

I don't know enough about astrology to give the details, but she seemed to have a great grasp of the constellations and the planets, and for her, they were aligned.

As she explained the wonders of this, I began to ponder if it was but a dream. Drunkenness may not give one a way with words, but it can enliven the mind. She spoke with great certainty, and I recall thinking how lucky she would be if I had offered to shag her. She seemed to pull this from my mind as well.

"He will be here to pick me up." She said, "I don't have much longer to wait."

Part of me wondered if this meant "Hurry!" and I sat up dutifully.

"He can see us."

I looked around wondering.

She pointed again to the sky.

"I have to be true to him. They know."

It was at that moment that I knew that she was feeling my pulse. She was drawing out my thoughts, just as I was trying to conceal them.

Her constant reference to Galactica and the planets and the constellations and how they were aligned had me on my heels. I was no longer cynical nor perverse nor flirtatious. I was listening and absorbing what she was communicating to me.

And then she was gone.

I awoke with her words echoing in my head. I felt invigorated, as one feels when they come out of a cold shower.

"He will come."

"He will come."

I scrambled for my glasses only to find that they were still on my face. The smeared lenses that had blurred my vision were clear, maybe too clear. Confusion and doubt filled my head. I must have rubbed them clean at some point. I took them off my face only to realize that one of the arms was no longer attached to the lens frame. The tiny screw that had held it to them had disappeared. I recalled that she had mentioned that they sometimes came, whoever they were, when their spaceships needed repair. I knew that somehow somewhere, there was a spacecraft that had come from wherever they do for a tiny screw that needed to be taken from one who would believe.

The bus pulled up moments later. I got on as is sometimes said, "Like a boss." There was no hesitation or stumbling or staggering. I strode onto the bus and whipped out the roll of bills from my pocket. They were neatly arranged with the smallest denominations on the inside of the bankroll. I paid the fare and recalled what the man from Gloucester had said. "I will be damned if I am going to buy those thieving money changers a drink." And vowed that I would spend them all in the airport. I sat three seats behind the driver thinking I needed to be at least that far away to hide the smell of alcohol that I knew was permeating the air yet my mouth felt clean, as though I had just brushed my teeth and as I stealthily gave myself a visual check, all of the buttons of my Levi 501s were attached and buttoned and a glance at the driver's mirror let me know that my face had not fallen off as the man from Gloucester suggested it might as a result of the re-labeled bootleg brandy that he had complained we were drinking.

At the first stop, I was expecting awful looks from folks who were boarding. I was sure they would know that I had been consuming great quantities of alcohol and I imagined that the smell was horrific. I figured that I was still drunk as I knew that I was in for a relentless hangover…but there was none of that. I could smell the Davidoff cologne that I wore, and I was still amazed that my mouth felt like I had just come from a dentist. I no longer feared the consternation that I felt when sitting next to a drunk. I knew that I had experienced something special. I smiled as I imagined the hippy woman brushing my teeth. cleaning me up and giving me a spritz from the cologne that I had in my pocket for just such an emergency. Or had I been abducted?

When I picked up my baggage from the lockers, the heat had been replaced by a morning chill, the champagne bottle was cool, probably the same temperature as when I took it from the wine cellar. "Siempre hay un primero ves." was not a warning but a salutation. Spain is a magical place.

The Framing of Pollock

The hatred engendered was not his intention
The greatness for which he strived was yet his mortal
enemy
His behaviour was contrived as he struggled for fame in
infamy
Couldn't sell a painting to save his life with a smile she
said
He didn't hear it. He was already dead.
Folks blame him for taking two souls
But who was there to save his?
Backstabbers and thieves, criticizing his every move
while planning theirs
His greatness lives on, their fortunes intact
His life had no value, his work saved the day
Those in the know, their fortunes they pay
For brushes without strokes, paint that splattered
Who owned this or that? That is what mattered.
His work stays amazing in a world full of hurt.
Buy art from the live ones, said a man named Kirk[1]

---

[1] "The biggest spur to my interest in art came when I played van Gogh in the biographical film Lust For Life. The role affected me deeply. I was haunted by this talented genius who took his own life, thinking he was a failure. How terrible to paint pictures and feel that no one wants them… This is what stimulated my interest in buying works of art from living artists. I want them to know while they are alive that I enjoy their paintings hanging on my walls, or their sculptures decorating my garden."
Kirk Douglas from **"Climbing The Mountain: My Search For Meaning"**

Heed not his advice; critique his films.
Your comments important, his legacy fulfilled.
Jackson is dead, long live his work.
In death art's a hero, in life it's a jerk.

Chronicle of a memory

Before social media, photos were a burden. As I try to collect some of my memories, I recognize that we are now twenty years into the new century. Though I never thought this when I was living the history rather than studying it, 1990 was certainly as different from 2020 as 1890 was from 1920. I recall meeting people and exchanging actual addresses so that we could send letters and photos as what is now called snail mail. Things were more tangible as a month seemed so short while now it seems an eternity. As I see artists post work after work after work on social media, I wonder if their work has any importance at all, especially to them.

It is important for an artist to stay grounded, particularly one who has failed. I was never one for the cocked beret and scarf, but I have found myself peering at my reflection and catching myself impressed. I had a long coat, similar to a duster, that a friend had loaned while I was in Paris. I had a pair of Tony Lamas that were about 15 years old. I still have them now, but they are forty. They are a light jaune, one of my favourite colours of oil paint. They were quite notable when I was wearing blue jeans, The borrowed long coat complimented them well as the collar nearly matched their colour.

As I witnessed myself in the narrow window of the train, I pulled out, not a mobile phone, but my notebook and pen. I imagined myself in an advertisement for a men's magazine. I suppose if this had occurred in 2015 rather than 1995, I would have quickly taken a selfie... She was American from Stockton or Fresno or somewhere near the bay area but not San Francisco. She probably told me her name and the place that she was staying but I do not remember these details nor would I at the time, these were those subtle hints that women throw out and men refuse to catch as they busy themselves talking about themselves without the good sense to shut up. She had a magnificent Asian face; the kind that will never look old, beautifully rounded save for the sharpness of her cheeks and chin. I think she said her parents came from Korea. She spoke with a California accent and offered me some raisins that were packaged in Fresno and, come to think of it, that probably was her hometown. She disappeared seemingly into thin air.

This is somewhat of an expectation of mine whenever I meet an interesting female, so I wasn't surprised. I was surprised when she returned with a map of the cemetery, opened it, and held it so close to my face that her face touched mine when we turned to look at each other. It would have been an excellent moment for a kiss had I been less absorbed in myself and the fact that I had landed this fish.

Were I a fisherman however, I would have learned by then to be more careful and make certain that the fish was not only landed but safely on ice before I began my igno-rant assed soliloquy about life in France and what the hell I was doing in Paris. And any woman who reads this will tell you that I was in fact talking to myself. Women pre-tend to but do not listen to men because they are gener-ous. What most men don't realize is that women don't listen to us because about ninety percent of what we spew is pure bullshit and not very clever bullshit at that.

Most women pretty much wait for us to talk that particu-lar head off so that we can hopefully redeem ourselves later when we finally get around to that for which the woman approached us in the first place. And for most women on vacation, I would guess that they figure the stupider we sound, the less likely they will feel bad when they dump us after a short torrid "romance" otherwise known as a "Good time". Well as luck would have it, about an hour later, the soliloquy turned into a discourse as I argued the finer points of my own stupidity, complementing myself on my expertise at losing the landed catch. "And a fine one she was." A voice noted..."and there will be others even finer." The same voice replied. A single pair of footsteps pounded firmly on the path as I rambled on alone.

What men think are good lines are about as original as clear glass and equally as transparent.

Write

"Just go man!" I said to myself as I pushed into another writing session. I had been creating some backgrounds for some new paintings by painting over some older works that I just couldn't stand. Economics had come into the picture as a year away from a paying job was teaching me to economize. I thought of how spoiled I was when I could stride into, Hoa Si, the art shop next to the Fine Arts University and empty the place of canvas and paint was I to have the mind to. Now, I am hard pressed to buy materials without wondering what I am going to eat for the next couple of days.

There are basically two types of people who buy at Hoa Si. I don't say shop because there is no shopping. Folks come there with a purpose, whether they are the rich local artists who basically have a lifetime endowment due to their family connections, or the students, some of whom are truly poor, the buyers come for specific tools of their trade regardless of their economic state.

Whether it is sad or not, the most talented of the working-class artists eventually graduate from art school and immediately take on jobs that carry them far away from their passion. And those who have the means to have great training and the cash to continue go on to earn sinecures in their family businesses and sideline themselves claiming this is owing to the reality that art is a profitless passion, in other words, it is work.

I tend to pound the keys of my laptop. I suppose that comes from my days of working with an actual typewriter, something that a younger generation cannot know. This is not to demean the younger generation; it is merely an observation.

Working hard no longer means to labour. There is no dignity in this. Working smarter not harder is the key. A techie putting in many hours, cleverly avoiding physical labour is considered a hard-working soul. A session at the gym has replaced the physical work that built muscle and character. A six pack is the reward, a dynamite body and a phony demeanour, for time spent at a gym. The thought of working for a living has been deleted from our core values. It has been replaced by the pursuit of leisure, which is the goal of the modern. Work is now depicted as time on a beach or in a luxury residence with a laptop and mobile phone or just a mobile phone and a cocktail.

I was trying to come up with a story that would appeal to the failed artists of the world to let them know that the world had not abandoned them. I thought of Van Gogh, who took his ear and later his life, as his sacrifice to humanity. Certainly, he suffered insanity or maybe sanity, but his lines were true. He worked.

As I was looking at some of the works I have created, I hearken the images that drove me to my obsession in the first place. A bit of self-loathing seemed in order.

"Was I selling out?" I wondered. "Was I burning out??"

"What the hell was I doing there?" I thought. I was recalling a recent evening of clubbing in bars where I was so out of my element both in age and style that it seemed the host at one of the places was wondering whether or not she was going to have to call an EMT to revive me if I was to have another drink. All if this was done in the sake of "networking". It shocked me knowing that I could shock her with an idea that could almost literally blow her mind. The young tend to think the old dead of mind, unworthy of new, especially in the realm of ideas. Trying to wrap one's head around another's resistance to learning becomes a cycle. Are they resisting or is it me?

The shades of green in one of my paintings brings thoughts of the natural world though nature is absent in the image. There is a floral accent to it though and I have wondered why that is not always present to the viewer. I recommended the piece for an exhibition some time ago, but the curators were not interested. They commented on the many moods of my work but were not moved by the mood of this one.

It is a bit like a Chagall, I suppose that comes from the fact that I often visited the Chagall Museum when I lived in Nice, France but it has a hint of Matisse, another former resident of the Cote de Azur.

I suspect that my work has become contrived. This is something that must be battled. To say defeated would be incorrect, an understatement as it is a moment-by-moment battle that is never fought and never won. Contrived itself is a borrowed word. My use of it is as contrived as it is contemptuous. A steady diet of contempt is healthy for an artist though. One can easily create many excuses. Good work is a bit more difficult.

*Nice (2017) Oil on Canvas 120 cm x 100 cm From **The Mind Garden Collection***

Never Again

I can't remember when or why I said this, but I said I would never sell another painting. Obviously, this can be an oath of honour or resignation. It could be that I was resigning myself to the situation I was in. I hadn't sold a painting for ages, and I just couldn't fathom the energy that I would have to have to even make an attempt at a sale. Posting things online has probably been the most futile. But not far in second place is the face to face when one of the few visitors that came to my gallery which was so far away from the centre of the city, I felt like giving anyone who came out there some sort of prize for their determination and logistical skills. There were also the curious from the neighbourhood who would pop in in what usually seemed a kind of a test of my language skills or a display of their own. English may be a popular field of study, but it is mostly an excuse for meeting foreigners or for children whose folks want to rid themselves of their kids for a few hours a week.

The strangeness of some of the encounters at my gallery was becoming a point of frustration for me. I have a certain talent for sales, but I lack the ability to use those skills to sell my own work. And then there is a cultural barrier. I have been told on several occasions that a buyer cannot bargain with the artist. Though it is apparently meant as a sign of respect, it seems to put the creator of art at the mercy of a salesperson, and this seems unjust at best.

I am certain that many galleries have talented salespeople and gallery owners are good at sales, but it seems a bit illogical to me. The assumption that a third party determines the value of my work is more than a bit unsettling.

And in my experience, it has been a terrible idea. I could give an anecdote or two, but it just seems uninteresting and a bit like inventing excuses.

Certainly, it can be degrading to have a person challenging me on the price of my work but for the most part, I have found pleasure in conversations about the value the work has for the buyer and their motives for a purchase. A couple of my favourite sales have also been the least rewarding financially. Having said this though, it is often nice to have a buffer, a salesperson who can deal with that which I would rather not. But it can be alarming when the person who is supposed to be advocating for me decides that my work is not that valuable even when the buyer is prepared to pay a premium price. And, unfortunately, sometimes that person is me.

Exhibitions can be brutal, and I usually end up embarrassed, drunk or both as the atmosphere is so contrived, I feel like I am the phoniest of phonies, a role I play quite well. Markets are worse as people tend to roam around them, just like commenters on social media, popping in at the least convenient times to make the inanest commentaries. And God forbid that a friend or "client" of another artist at a market or exhibit shows any interest in a competing artist's work as it seems the friendly, casual atmosphere turns into a zero-sum game which no one wants to lose.

I used to say that I am not playing defence and that I am happy when another artist's work sells. I believe that the more art sales there are, the more likely I will sell something. Perhaps this could be called the law of abundance? I heard a great TedTalk where some high-flying CEO was explaining the concept of freedom from fear to an audience. He used an example, probably made up, most examples using percentages are, where he said that graduating students at Harvard University were given two hypothetical options. In one they could make 160,000 USD per year and everyone else in the class would make 140,000. The other option was that everyone else would make 240,000 and they would make 220,000. He went on to say that 87% chose the first option and to enhance the understanding of the audience and draw out the obligatory laughter, he said, and these are supposed to be smart people. I am certain that, had he taken a poll of the audience, he could have achieved similar results especially if the situation was actually a reality. If they were all there for a sort of group job interview, I could imagine many of them, maybe most, choosing the "winning" option even after his speech.

I found myself repeating my pledge to never sell another painting. The recognition that being guided by an imaginary marketplace is no way to create has come crashing down on me once more.

A local doctor that I had met at a wine tasting came by. I had rented a new space in the centre of town to attract more visitors. He seemed a bit confused. Real Estate in this area of the city is extremely expensive and the good doctor had decided before he came that the gallery would be immense and elaborately adorned. His confusion was matched by my own, I was wondering how he thought I could afford such a space. Despite the fact that I know from experience that art is a diversion of the rich, I still carry on with the myth that one can enrich the world through art. But one must be successful to be a success and though I have heard it said that no one wants to miss the next Van Gogh, I think the contrary is true. No one wants to find the next Van Gogh, unless that Van Gogh is wealthy enough to purchase a piece of the long dead Van Gogh's work. While this may be a bit of an exaggeration, I think it a bare-naked fact that "art lovers" love artists who have either already found fame in another medium, like acting, or are well heeled enough that they would not embarrass a client at a dinner party or a political fund raiser. The rich invest while the poor waste. The simplicity of my gallery was obviously lost on him. Economizing is for the wealthy, if I had a Bentley parked in front of the place, I think he could have understood my thrift.

I had brought a painting that I truly love from my home to this new space. I was a bit excited to have it displayed in public after having it carefully hidden away in my home for the last two years or so. I had been very protective of it, probably overprotective. I didn't want to hang it as I wanted to give it a bit of an introduction before I put it on the wall. I had hoped a special client would come by and the good doctor seemed like a perfect fit for the work. I had it propped up on a bench and I thought it would be the most appropriate piece of my work for him, judging by the work that I had seen displayed in his house.

"That is not your work." He said curtly and he passed it by like it was some sort of enemy flag. I wondered if he actually meant that it was not my work or not my style. He would later pause in front of another piece and say, "Pollock. You are influenced by Pollock." I lamely told him that it was more like a Tancredi than a Pollock and mentioned that it was not a drip painting. I recognized that I needed the sale so I hurriedly said, no less lamely, yes, one can see that in the lighting. The whites and greys bring out the truth in the colours", I lied. He seemed ready to buy but I made what I thought an innocuous comment about the frame, and he replied that one can get frames anywhere and actually threw his hands up in the air as his sign that he was exasperated and had enough.

When he was leaving, he shouted two promises, which sounded more like threats, first to visit my home and then to invite me to his to drink whiskey. I had been to his house before and I hoped to have a second chance with the "Pollock". After he had mounted his scooter, a crappy old Japanese model which looked a lot more appropriate in front of my humble gallery than any Rolls Royce would, he pulled on his helmet with both hands like he was trying to crush his own neck. I rushed out with a painting of a pomelo which I had painted some years ago.

While at a prior meeting in his home he recounted a story about his mother. It was the typical rags to riches story that one hears from the wealthy. The setting for the telling of the story was in front of a pomelo tree in front of his house which he had planted in memory of his dear mother. My act was truthful and sincere, but his story suddenly seemed an invention. He carelessly tossed the painting into the front basket of his scooter like I had given him a piece of soiled toilet paper.

As he rode away with all the grace of a middle finger in one's face, I thought of another oath. Don't ever give a painting away! I have screamed this to myself on several occasions. And once again, I had succeeded at failure. But even at failure, one has a second chance. Maybe that is one of the greatest things about failure. There are so many ways to achieve it.

The Perfection of Pollock *(2018) Oil on Canvas 80 cm x 60 cm*

The ten best

Should I make a list? I thought.

Lists are all the rage. I continued to myself. "All the rage?" You mean they go viral. I self-corrected.

The Top Ten Reasons to Become a Failure (In no particular order)

1. Failing is fun. Nothing like getting up in the morning realizing that there is no real reason to be awake. Awake, asleep or dead, it's all the same! The only difference is, when one is awake, those nightmares and the self-loathing that goes with them come to life! They are real! You really have lost at the game of life and will continue to as long as you live! Sleep away! Getting up early is for those who simply can't accept failure.

2. Failure is happiness. Nothing better when reliving the glory days of one's younger life than actually recognizing that there is such a thing as "the good old days". Virtually any memory is fonder than the present reality. Even more so when those memories are of past failures. There is nothing quite like reminiscing about what could have been. And there will be plenty more of this in the future if you can just keep on failing!

3. Failure is honesty. Imagine having to tell one of those shitty rags to riches success stories that every wealthy person burdens him or herself with... No need! You can be completely honest! Some live a life while some live a lie! I remember listening to an inspirational speaker talk about the

savage hardships that he had to overcome as a youth. I was amazed at his perseverance. And I was surprised about twenty years later when I heard the same guy telling a much different story! He is now so rich that he no longer needs such a story and in fact doesn't want one as now he wants pedigree! A failure can be a mutt or a pure-bred, there is purity in all that is failure.

4. Failure is integrity. Human dignity! That's what you have. Like some dog crap on the bottom of one's shoe you adorn the world with the purity of your presence. You needn't pretend importance as you permeate the very air that the successful breathe. Their claims that failure brought them to where they are today seem about as sincere and heart felt as a second-hand greeting card. They thank failure. Fail big they say! And when you do succeed, rub it in! Save yourself from this shallow, contemptuous nonsense; long live the failures!

5. It's enough! Five out of ten! Four out of ten! Being a failure means you don't have to finish!

Compettyness

I have coined a word, perhaps invented it "compettyness". One of the things that I have a very difficult time coming to terms with is the zero-sum game that seems to be the dominant strategy of virtually any human endeavour with which I am familiar. Whether it is dating where folks seem only to be interested in the person that another is interested in or business where it seems that the most important thing is to be in front of a "competitor" so that he can be held back rather than moving forward in one's own direction. I see this again and again, particularly when one company buys another. They lay waste to a previously functioning entity as though they are proving that it wasn't worthy of their purchase in the first place. When I mention this, it is explained to me in the old "dog eat dog" expression or the person simply says something to the effect that humans are competitive which seems more repetitive than logical.

Sometime ago, I was stalked by a man named Don who painted and apparently sought me out because he had seen some of my posts on social media. He was relentless in his invitations to meet and insistent that we met at his house. I thought it great as I am always looking for artists with whom I can collaborate. I was hoping to build an art community here in Hanoi and worldwide for that matter.

I had a full-time job as a teacher, at that time, and he was basically being supported by his wife who was also a teacher albeit at a different school. He said he was fascinated by the fact that I was working at art commercially, meaning that I was actively showing and selling my work. He couldn't understand why as I had a regular job with a good salary. He was a bit vague, and I guessed he was complimenting me on my diligence.

I thought it was a kind of collegial respect that he was demonstrating as he showed me his work and bragged of a buyer that he had in Taiwan. He mentioned that he worked with a one of the posh uptown galleries, that he could not name, which regularly sold his work locally and he had even had a piece on display in the Opera House which he fancied an achievement and said that he wished he had actually seen it so he could have been even more proud.

His manner was changing as he admitted me into his world though he seemed rather secretive, and I began to wonder about his motives for seeking me out. I started to suspect that he was going to drop some sort of bomb. I thought he might introduce the idea of him selling my work on commission, maybe even under his name. He mentioned the amount of time that it took him to produce works and bits of his methods and it seemed he was selling so much that he was behind in his production. As he showed me around, it was obvious that he was tracing some other's works, he had a painting of a bicycle which looked so much like so many I have seen here that I guessed it was a reproduction.

It became apparent to me that I wasn't really part of the conversation as it was rapidly becoming the monologue that I have become so accustomed to these days. He was telling. There was no exchange. His telling became a sort of persuasive speech about the difficulties that a working artist has making a living, caused by those who did not need to make a living through art but were competing against them. I was a bit baffled as I still was stuck in the idea that he wanted to collaborate.

He said, "People who have jobs like you, just go home after work. They make dinner, eat, watch TV, and go to bed. Why don't you do this?"

Without waiting for a reply, he continued. "My wife makes a great salary. She supports me and it is very difficult to support myself with my work. You don't need to make money, why are you trying so hard?"

I left his house, without making any effort to respond. He had shooed me out, as he busied himself with washing some teacups and explaining his day-to-day routine. It was though he thought that by changing the subject he had had the final word and there was nothing more to discuss. As he had laboured away, I had promised myself that I would avoid him despite a kind of naïve notion that I had misunderstood him.

A few weeks later, I was having a small show at a funky place called Apache; its white walls and cathedral ceiling made it a fabulous venue. Among the usual notes that one gets on Messenger, congratulating one on an achievement while noting that the sender cannot attend the ceremony celebrating that achievement as they have something much more important to do, I found a note from Don! I rarely have the good sense to block folks like him so there he was! He mentioned that he would be too busy to attend the opening but thanked me for the invitation which I could not recall sending him. He said he would meet me there the following Monday in the morning. I replied that I could not be there, which he already knew as it was a workday for teachers like me and his wife.

I came by Apache on that Monday afternoon to check-in and give the folks some fliers to hand out. The manager, a young hip Vietnamese guy, blurted out, "Your friend was here!" I recognized the angst on his face, and I relieved it by saying, "He is not my friend."

"I didn't think so. He came before we were even open. He was actually waiting outside. He didn't even let me open the door before he told me that he was artist and he was pushing his smart phone in my face, trying to show me photos. I couldn't get the key in the lock."

I chuckled as I thought. "You just can't make this stuff up." He was incredulous that I was smiling.

"He's asshole!" he exclaimed, in the way the young and hip second language folks always seem to do, as they dominate the vocabulary of profanity even when they lack the grammar to use it properly.

"He didn't even go upstairs to look at your work!"

"He didn't come to see my work." I said, "He came to convince you to take it down."

"But he don't even say that. He don't even say he wants he wants his work here."

"He doesn't." I replied, "He just doesn't want mine here."

The look on his face was priceless and he had definitely lost his hippy cool. "What the hell is wrong with him?"

"Envy." I said. "He envies me. He skipped right past jealousy to envy."

The tattooed youth just cringed as he squeezed his face with his palms and shook his head.

"I know. I know." I said trying to comfort him. "I am not exactly an object of envy but he is compettytive."

"You mean competitive." Like any good second language speaker, he took the opportunity to correct.

"No. It's my word. Most people don't compete. They just go around talking shit about others rather than doing anything themselves. Do you know what a cockblock is?"

I knew he would enjoy this concept, which was not unfamiliar to him though he did not know the term. I continued with this impromptu counselling session as I knew he had been damaged. I used to call this compettytiveness "playing defence" but I recognized it was easier to understand if I put it in terms of the zero-sum game. Competition is such a worn-out concept. It is like the holey jeans that became so trendy, holy to the rich.

I had always said that the rich don't want what they have they want what the poor have. Their belief that the poor want what they have is merely their enveloping poor folks with their economic "science" and "philosophy". Sadly, it seems more human than rich as wealth does not trickle down, but idiocy certainly does. I have rarely met a wealthy person who does not tell me that they "envy" me for being able to be an artist while complaining that they had to forsake such a "passion" because they had to be practical. This is usually augmented with an explanation of why they can't buy a piece of my work and a story about how they support young artists by purchasing their works for virtually nothing. It is all about inspiration at the end of the day. There is nothing more inspiring than the failure to make a living at one's craft. And failure is a must in the art world leaving very little room for success...

Exhibitionist

Though I regularly seek out places to exhibit my work, I rarely enjoy exhibitions. I think they are appropriately named as they do bare one's soul and I often feel quite naked. Even when I want to feel comfortable and cool, the feeling that I am exposed is not unlike the feeling one might have recognizing a zipper is open on one's pants. And, in an effort to feel more comfortable, I often seek the comfort of a drink or two which usually leads to a bout with intoxication. And then there is the intoxication of being the centre of attention even when exhibiting in a larger exhibition where, in fact, I am virtually anonymous.

Through a connection, I was invited to an exhibition, touted to be the most prestigious in Vietnam. I guesstimate there were about fifty artists exhibiting, probably 48 who were Vietnamese. The couple who was curating the event were friends of a friend and I thought of it as mutually beneficial for both of us; I would get exposure in a great event, and they would get another foreign artist to give validity to the international character they were advertising.

It was a bit of a heady experience to have them come to my home, a small, white European style cottage on a street called Dang Thai Mai, in Tay Ho, which is largely a refuge for expats and the hip rich of Hanoi. As they mosied around the place which was filled wall to wall with paintings, they wandered to the rear of the house where I create. Before entering, much as one might ask for permission to use another's restroom, they asked whether they could come in.

Phuong, my friend, asked me as though I needed translation of their request, and I replied, "Of course! I knew they would want to see the studio." I was rather proud when they entered but as they peered around the disarray, I thought I felt a hint of contempt. I made the obligatory apology about pardoning the mess and Thu, the friend of my friend, replied, "We knew it would be like this." The hint of contempt that I felt seemed to be mirrored in the faces of Thu and her husband Do, a tall thin man who had allegedly given up his passion to create in order to promote. I was a bit taken aback as I assumed that it seemed quite judgemental, especially coming from folks who regarded themselves as "open-minded art lovers".

I have learned that facial expressions often give lie to the truth and truth to the lie and hoped mine did not betray me. I began to wonder about their motives though I maintained the naïve enthusiasm that has allowed me to be conned so often in life that I have sometimes wondered if this is where the Connors family name found its origins.

As they went through page after page of my life turning through the stacks of paintings like so many pages of a book, they stopped once or twice. I tried to encourage Phuong to encourage them to go back out to the display area as I had already chosen the work that I wanted to be exhibited.

"You have many moods!" commented Do. This was translated from Vietnamese but in "artese" it means "You don't have a style." You see, or maybe you don't, artists are supposed to have a style that anyone can easily associate with them. In order to be great, one must create! In order to create one must replicate! An artist must settle into a niche and pound that niche until he has squeezed

172

out every last strand of his creative DNA. It is a kind of branding process not unlike that of cattlemen. One must declare, "Those cows in that herd are mine!" And, perhaps, that is what separates an accomplished artist from a failed artist, the ability to recreate one's own creations.

My enthusiastic naiveté was rapidly being replaced by angst, though I should refrain from using such a word understanding that this is a feeling that might describe a condition of a true artist. Perhaps a gentle feeling of panic might suit me better; the process had become excruciating. And like one who has had one too many jolts of caffeine, I began to murmur. My murmuring was as much a product of the triad that had replaced the foursome that entered the small space as I felt myself absent though I was obviously still there. This has not been uncommon in my travels as ignorant locals often speak as though a foreigner needs translation regardless of one's level of language skills in the local language. And the ignorance grows exponentially with the competence of the foreigner. It seems a product of insecurity.

They chose two pieces which were a bit dark, and were good impressions of the range of feelings that I was experiencing at the moment. I suppose paranoia could assign this to my suspicion that this was how they meant me to feel or perhaps clairvoyance as it was certainly a sign of things to come.

Delivering the paintings was a challenge. Like most major cities Hanoi is a maze and access to the building's parking lot was much better suited to the motorbikes which dominate the streets here, than to the Chevrolet Spark that was my vehicle. I was still healing from the explosion of the top of my tibia which occurred as a result of an accident on one those aforementioned motorbikes.

I have learned to ignore parking attendants and such as it doesn't matter where one parks here, it is not in the right place. I maneuvered my vehicle onto a ramp in front of the building and proceeded to hobble out of my car; rip the small 60 x 80 paintings out of the back and do a kind of one-legged hop up the stairs as the security guard waved me in asserting his presence by allowing me to do that which I was obviously already inclined. I managed to drop the paintings with an attendee who seemed to wonder why I was even there as I wondered what the hell she would be wondering about as she was assisting in an art exhibition. I suppose I could have been randomly dropping paintings with high hopes or maybe she didn't recognize them as paintings considering the works of the giants of the art world whose works would also be on display there.

The opening came with much fanfare, and I even noticed that they had used one of my works to fill a tiny spot, about one half inch square, in their colourful pamphlet. At first, I didn't notice but when one of my cynical students who had done me the honour to attend, laughingly pointed it out, squeezing her fingers together like it was the measure of the size of my penis. I chuckled knowingly as I recalled my past episode of clairvoyance. As I ambled around the exhibits, I wondered where they had put my work as it was not in the area that had been labelled "Abstract". And then the cameras came. The gay producer whose models would be opening the show came by to give me a shove and tell me to get out of the way. I wondered what way I supposed to get out of as I was not even close the red carpet they were using as a runway. The lights dimmed and then flashed in the brilliance of the obligatory light show that seems to be part of any event here. As the models strode down the runway with

174

the patented grimace that has become the face of modelling, I was to receive yet another shove as I was in the only space that the producer needed whenever he would pass.

Things calmed down after the lights went back on and folks began to meander from place to place. My cynical student came to me and introduced me to her grandfather, a former local dignitary, assuring me that he did not come to see my work but rather that of a famous Vietnamese artist that was showing. Her mother was a bit more gracious though she did not comment on my presence or work, and I began to feel a bit "set up".

Thu, the organizer came a stood next to my token foreign ass for a few photos and politely pointed to the corner where my work was displayed. When I arrived there, I was shocked. My 60 by 80s looked incredibly tiny next to an immense realistic work of about three meters by four. I started to understand their choice as my works had come from a collection called "Mind Garden" which is inspired by the local shapes and colours of the flower markets and could probably be construed as an attempt at floral realism. I was horrified as I waited for the camera crew just as I had been instructed. But, as I have learned many times in my life "For sudden, the worst turns the best to the brave". A foreign couple, most likely of mixed nationalities as they were conversing in heavily accented English, stood next to me and, ignoring the large piece, began to admire mine. The man said to the woman, "You see! These young Vietnamese artists are so creative!" She agreed. Apparently near sighted he put on a pair of glasses to get a look at the title and my name, which was to the great joy of my cynical student, misspelled…twice. Creative City was the name of the place, so I thought this appropriate as they had creatively spelled it two different ways and accidentally left my web address off the tag.

"Oh nuts! He's a foreigner." The man exclaimed as he pushed his face toward the tag. It was loud enough that I could have heard it if I was back in the special place of the pushy producer. I suddenly wished that my cynical student was still there as she was robbed of this moment of glory. As I tried not to look into the microphone that the attractive reporter held near face, the journalist hid her face as though she and the "Oh nuts" man were soul mates. Still, I spoke confidently. One of the most precious responsibilities of a failed artist must always be to embrace failure as though it is a goal. Acceptance is for the pusillanimous, a true failure must relish his role. He must seek to fail at all costs. His failures must be as grandiose as they are non-existent. Anonymity is the reward for one's success. One's success must be punished with anonymity. One's existence must be denied flagrantly for one to be a true failure. One must be obsessed with failure.

Mind Garden 56: Dark Thoughts *2015 Oil on Canvas 80 cm x 60 cm From **The Mind Garden Collection***

The Seller

I often see lists, like top ten lists, on people's blogs and such. They have always been popular, but it seems they have now become so abundant that one can find a list of virtually anything that could possibly be commented on. Top ten places to go for adventure, becomes a more focused list of something like Top Ten places to go for adventure which won't put your life at risk or for those more adventurous, Top Ten Places to go for adventures which could send you off with a bang! Anyway, I am certain, if I cared to look there are lists on things to avoid when selling art and things one must do to sell art and how to price art and and and. I could make hundreds of them myself. But here are my top tips!

How not to approach a potential buyer: The way I do. I am not sure how I attained this skill. I had been very successful selling other people's things when my livelihood depended on it. Now that my actual life depends on it, I have become quite proficient at turning off potential buyers. Granted, I am less young and apparently less charming but blaming it on my age would be far too generous. It would be allowing the jerk that crawls out of me when I meet new folks to escape unscathed. It is partly arrogance and part experience that has brought me to this point. Here are the top three things that I do to turn off potential buyers.

1. Be vague about prices. This does not mean that I don't have a decent, easily understood pricing system but rather than I don't have it tattooed somewhere on me or have a sort of register that I could carry around that printed out price lists

whenever I am asked. Most of my sales are not from folks visiting my gallery but rather from networking. So those wise folks whose opinions and advice are priceless to themselves except when applying them to themselves can keep the "just put tags on them" and "put the prices on the website" advice to themselves as they are the types who usually make the process difficult. When I say that I am vague, I mean that I give high and low ranges, upon hearing this, a potential buyer is apparently sent to a kind of wonderland because it is just too confusing! How could it not be??? I mean when I go into a car dealership, all the cars are the same price aren't they? I am sometimes confused as to why shoes are not priced by size. Why shouldn't they be? Don't short people with small feet have to endure enough in this life without having to pay a kind of communal price for objects which shouldn't have the same production cost due to the fact that less material is used??? More of them can fit into a shipping container for gosh sakes! Are you telling me that capitalist economics really is nonsense and not a true science??? Oh... You have an explanation or at least an excuse? I don't! For whatever reason, with me a price range seems to derange folks. And trying to explain the obvious to one who is already confused by it is a bit of an uphill battle if not an impossibility.

2. Be even more vague about prices: Once it has been determined that your prices are too high, despite the fact that they are unknown, allow the potential customer to guide you. The customer is, after all, always right. And this is true because

some idiots pioneered the concept to get their employees to stop thinking for themselves and it has been repeated as though it is an absolute truth ever since. The customer is often wrong...very wrong. I have known many folks in the food and beverage industry. Some of them seem so guided by this "idea" that the customer is always right that they have gone from having a very clear concept to a kind of tortured version of what was their original idea. I have been such a regular customer at some places that the owners and management will come and discuss the intricacies or their businesses with me. I am shocked when they explain to me that something that was a speciality of theirs and a favourite of mine had been changed to suit their "customers". A sauce was too spicy or not spicy enough or just right but not right for the meat or vegetable with which it was being served. This is usually a signal to me that I will no longer be going to the place. Not because my opinion doesn't seem to matter, but rather that the place will not survive. There is a reason that consistency works. Those same folks will complain about customer complaints, but it is their response to those complaints makes any sort of leadership decision in the place to be null and void. I know of other folks who basically say, "Forget about the customer!" and for some crazy reason, their places not only survive but thrive. This is not because they don't care about their customers, on the contrary they care so much about them that they are willing to stick to their guns and serve food as they know best. And their best is much better when they don't respond to the overwhelmingly petty online reviews that haunt the digital world. And when it comes to art, it can be even worse.

A stock conversation about pricing goes as follows. I am introduced as an artist to someone, usually the partner of a man or woman who appreciates my work. The wife, husband, lover placates the person who introduces me by being open-minded and welcoming a look at my work on my website. He or she will mention that they love it, the person who introduced them to me will nod and maybe even wink. This assures him or her that I will get along with their mate and they can leave us alone. It assures me that a knife is on its way to my back as I know what they don't yet know. Their mate proceeds to tell me that he or she knows many artists, this is not only to put me in my place but also their mate; whether folks like it or not, most relationships have more to do with a struggle for power than anything to do with love. How dare he or she think that she or he knows a talented artist!!! This will result in a display of a piece of trash that he or she has commissioned from some poor young artist. This will be embarrassing, not to me but to the mate. You see, they are introducing me to the other half of their couple in an attempt to make their loving partner see a tiny bit of the light that might awaken him or her to the fact that buying crappy art from art students at prices that have the student working at near slave wages is not supporting the art world at all. It is merely convincing young artists that crap sells better than art and if they want to survive, they had better get used to producing it!

"What is your budget?" I will ask.

"Oh...I don't want to insult you." Usually, it is she in this conversation. This is a reference to the fact that she is from an affluent family, and she is so accustomed to insulting others that she thinks she has to explain that she would not lower herself to actually bother insulting me.

I always take the bait and rephrase the question. "What is your budget?" I will ask. To those who, having read the exact same words above, might think this an editorial error, think again! You see, or maybe you don't, my initial question, is about how much she is willing to spend, the second is how much she is able to spend. Once it has been made abundantly clear, that she is absolutely uninterested in spending one dime on anything that I could ever create and even less interested in spending one second longer discussing anything with me, I must recall the rule, the customer is always right, and continue on as though she was a potential customer. This "rephrasing" allows her the opportunity to explain to me something which the stupid man who introduced her to me already knows. She could pay whatever she pleases. Her parent's pedigree will be exposed. They both came from nothing and are incredibly protective of their daughter despite the fact that they spent gobs of money sending her around the world alone, since she was about fifteen, on a kind of life-time pleasure cruise. Before that, the parenting duties were left to a housekeeper or nanny as her parents were so busy working that they hardly had time to say hello to each other in the morning. Then the fact, that despite coming from nothing, the parents still managed to afford not only that nanny or housekeeper, but a mansion for her to keep along with a few villas for these hard-working folks and their lovers and friends. Private school fees were astronomical but after paying them her hardworking parents still managed to budget so they could send her on those frequent journeys she mentioned before and then a list of those journeys she will verbally compile for me as part of a lecture on her worldliness and her own struggle to the top, which is why she is so economical when it comes to buying anything from someone she actually knows. Her "budget" is reserved for buying expensive things from folks whose names are on labels and no one actually knows.

When she feels I am sufficiently educated on the fact that I am not, the lecture will end abruptly as though it had never begun. Her stated desire to not want to insult me has been fulfilled. I am unworthy of insult.

The male version is notably different in that, the male assumes that I have slept with the lady who introduces him to me. Whether I have or have not is irrelevant as the woman usually is not insistent on denying this as too firm a denial seems like a confession and awkward is awkward so there is no need in the first place. If he is taller than me, the male will use the word little a lot, and note that his daughter or niece or another female in the family is an artist in reference to it being a bit of a feminine pursuit, which is odd as this should put his suspicion that I have slept with his partner to rest but you know how artists are…

3. Be so vague about pricing that price is never even discussed! In the toolbox of the failed artist, one must keep handy that proverbial monkey wrench that one can toss into the fabled machine at any particular moment to crash that machine!

I Feel Fabulous

I was invited to a wine dinner not long ago and I was seated with a table of friends. I had been invited by a friend of these friends. I had come alone and was then been adopted by these friends. There was a gorgeous lady there unconnected to this crew who was being photographed for obvious reasons. She was so fashionable in dress that she would not be denied onlookers wherever she might be. Her stylish short black hair complimented the sharp features of her face perfecting her image as a kind of Asian princess. I would learn her name was Trang. As her eyes avoided the camera during a profile shot, they locked into mine. I was at first unsure whether she was using me as a focal point to avoid looking into the camera or showing interest, or both. When they finished their shoot, she made her way towards me and as she approached, I said, "You are fabulous!". She smiled and said a polite thank you and I repeated what I had said. We began chatting which drew the unwelcome attention of most of the rest of the males in the room. It ignited a cockblocking competition. One of the male waiters came over to tell us to take our seats. She and I said thank you and continued our conversation.

The waiter was insistent and truly rude as he desperately tried to get us to stop. I said "We both know that you want us to sit down. It is ok. We can sit down when WE want." The woman turned to him, repeated what I had said but with a kind of stutter that added an emphasis which a less elegant soul might have replaced with a bit of profanity. He reluctantly moved away from us. I asked my host if they would mind rearranging the seats. I said I want to sit by Trang, to which he replied, seeming a bit perturbed "I know! Everyone does!"

The table was set for about 20 and was being shared by about four different groups. The seat next to Trang was unoccupied and Fat Scott, the man who now seemed sorry that he had invited me was desperately trying to get the last invitee to come and he was actually physically blocking the seat by putting his arm around the back of the chair as he barked instructions to the missing guest into his phone. I am sometimes polite, and I did notice that Trang got a similar reception when she asked the sponsor of the event whether he could move a couple of people, so I minded my manners and stayed in my seat. I tried not to be awkward in my gaze towards her, but we somehow found fascination in each other and ended up trading a lot of smiles and a bit of chuckling. This was apparently annoying to a couple of the other males on my end of the table, so I began to chat with the lady next to me who was the wife of the man on the other side of her. I managed a kind of cheers and a goodbye glance and set down my wine glass and with a careless gesture; I managed to knock it over. Fortunately, the glass was full to the appropriate wine serving size so that there was enough in it to give the white t-shirt I had on a pretty good dousing.

I became the centre of attention and suddenly had one man throwing salt onto me straight out of the fancy silver saltshaker while the waiter scrubbed me with a napkin as others shouted out their laundering recommendations. The look on Trang's face was priceless. Absent of mockery, it was soft, even loving, like the look one might give a child to keep him from crying.

I have a hard time managing embarrassment out of such inevitable acts of buffoonery and I am sure she noted that, I was actually a bit amused by the situation. The design on the shirt advertising my art gallery wore the wine well. No one was awful about it, and I had come prepared with a long-sleeved shirt which had had worn unbuttoned over the t-shirt to bring me up to the smart casual dress code. I had an epiphany and recognized that I could button up the shirt and "Voila" no more wine stain!

I saw a bit of shock on her face when she realized that I was now wearing a button up shirt and I think she wondered how I pulled that one off. I noticed that she seemed to be trouble finishing her second course and I got up to have a word about the food. All was amazingly pleasant.

When I returned to my seat, the woman next to me had a question. We had been talking cuisine as folks do during such events and I had identified myself as having been in the food and beverage business and had a certain amount of expertise. Our next course was beef, and the cut was hanging tender. I did not know what hanging tender was. It was obviously the cut of beef, but I had no idea from what part of the cow. I began to Google it but then I turned and said in a very serious tone," Hanging tender is when the man can't get it up. The next course will be Viagra." Before I had time to realize what I just said and that we had just met, the woman exploded in laughter; literally exploded. The Gods were kind. Food did not fly from her face, but the force of her roar stirred the entire table. I joined her.

As I looked across the table to see Trang smiling but not laughing, I wondered if the joke was on me. As age has attacked my libido it has also savaged my ability. I guess it could be worse, but I feel that hanging tender has become a nearly constant state. I recall an expression "long and loose and full of juice" which meant that one was ready for anything. Loose was not meaning that one was soft, merely that things were swinging in the right direction. Hanging tender on the other hand ...well...I am not so sure that it is as admirable. Loosely speaking, I would have to say that hanging tender, while sounding a whole lot better than being a soft cock or having a limp dick could make one a bit weak as though injured. Hanging tender could mean that a man has been having it so often that he actually has rubbed himself raw, leaving him "hanging tender".

The show went on and visions of following up on the conquest of Trang became blurred as the wine began swirling around in my head. Wine dinners seem always to result in drunken affairs and by the time dessert had arrived, plans had been had made for the continuation of the debauchery at a different location. These plans included only my new friends and as we slurped down round after round at an expensive night club anything approaching the elegance with which the evening had begun was lost in the personal bouts of drunkenness as the group lost touch with reality and then one another. I don't recall leaving the place, but I do recall the emptiness that I felt in the taxi on my way home. I longed for the fabulous. I was left with nothingness.

Vietnamese is a tonal language. This means that it must be shouted out at the top of the speaker's lungs so that anyone within ten yards is left with their ears ringing from the tones...

Internet Begpackers

I flew in from Madrid. I was visiting some crazy friends in Ho Chi Minh City which some still like to call Saigon. I was taking a leisurely stroll to stretch my legs and get me out of the long flight funk. Jet lag is supposedly more pronounced when one flies east than west but I always seem to suffer a bit no matter which direction I fly.

I intended to check out some sites where I could pitch my work. I went by a hotel that happened to have some very pink furniture which I thought could be complimented by a couple very pink pieces that I have hanging in my friend's restaurant in District 1 and I took a few photos. I was feeling pretty good about this as this friend doesn't really enjoy the pink. I think this is as much a product of a kind of macho persona that he likes to exude as his personal taste. This is interesting to me. Some of my closest friends seem the furthest from me in their attitudes about masculinity and politics.

I was a bit lost as I wandered towards another destination. There was an artsy boutique hotel which I was seeking out though I wasn't quite sure I was going in the right direction. As I walked down a sidewalk that borders an upscale street market that caters mostly to the wealthier locals and expats who like to think they are mingling with them, I was suddenly accosted by one of those ex-pats.

I was wearing casual clothes. I wore a very red t-shirt I had picked up in Madrid at a tourist trap, so I had the name of that city prominently pasted on my chest. I had a pair of faded grey dress sweats which had seen better days, and some beat up grey Doc Martin loafers which matched the sweats in their state of wear.

Seemingly out of nowhere strode this tall frail nerd of a white guy. He held a phone pressed tightly to his ear and he began shouting into it.

"I've been here for fifteen years!" he shouted while looking straight at me. "It's getting disgusting! These begpackers are everywhere!"

It was a Sunday, and he was dressed like someone who had dressed up for something. His clothes looked like they still might have the price tags on them. He was almost shiny in appearance though he seemed rather dour in demeanour.

"I still can't believe it!" he continued. "It has become so lowbrow. I can't believe how lowbrow this place has become."

It was not suddenly that I recognized that he was talking about me as he stalked me from a distance of about two metres, and it was apparent that there was no one on the other end of his pretend phone conversation. It took a few moments to realize that he really was talking to me. It was kind of a process. Kind of like when a person leaves his house with an eye-catching stain on his clothes or face. It takes time to recognize that one isn't being admired when one gets attention. We all suffer from vanity.

He was taking kind of bounce steps as bounded from one side of the sidewalk to the other. I was not as annoyed as I could have been as he was as comical in his movement as he was in his manner. I sped up my stride and closed distance on him without any particular intention, this tripped him up, but he caught himself without falling. He gained courage in his embarrassment, and he stopped.

190

"Can you believe it?" he said. "This place is just full of begpackers."

"What is a begpacker?" I asked as though I didn't know.

"You know. Those people walking around looking for handouts."

"What people?" I said, looking around as though I was expecting to see one appear out of the thick humid air not failing to assess my own state by looking myself up and down.

He appeared puzzled and his imaginary phone partner must have died as he gave up the illusion that he was talking to someone else, and he spoke directly to me. "Begpackers are everywhere!"

"I just flew in from Madrid." I stated as I pointed at the decal on my t-shirt. "Do they have them there?"

"Huh?"

"M-A-D-R-I-D Madrid." I said spelling out the word on the decal with my finger.

He was obviously taken aback. "Oh... Madrid... That's a nice city."

The gods were kind and one of the made for film sets showers that only exist in the tropics began to toss down random drops of rain. And like a bucket of water being tossed into a fan they changed direction and flew directly in our faces.

"Hurry! We better get inside." He said ridiculously. The fact that there was no real inside in the market there made it even more ludicrous.

As he rushed away, I felt a bit abandoned, he had used the pronoun "we" after all and here he had left me alone. He flailed his arms like he was being attacked by hornets. As the warm drops of the shower mixed with my sweat, I continued my stroll unabated as though it was dry. I decided to hail a taxi after I stepped off a curb into the piss warm creek that the street had become. The motorbike taxi riders wearing their plastic suits waved empty plastic suits as they tried to hail me. I am not fond of them. I almost always feel it a life risk whenever I am riding on the back of a motorcycle, so I pretended to ignore them. The taxis ignored me. I supposed most of them were contracted to Grab or some other app service, so they were being selective. When one finally made its way away from the curb to pick me up, I realized it made sense to avoid the foolish foreigner who did not have the sense to get out of the rain.

As I sat down in the passenger seat the water squeezed out of my clothing; the driver seemed unconcerned by this. He was busy playing with his cell phone while we weaved down the flooded avenue.

The air-conditioner was blasting. There is only one temperature other than hot here, cold. There is no warm or cool. One is either being baked in the hot dry sun, steamed in the humidity, or quick frozen in an artificially refrigerated environment.

As my damp clothing surged from wet to frozen, I wondered if we all aren't begpackers. Every one of us who is on social media is constantly begging for attention and God forbid we reciprocate. Our hand is out to take not to give. Having a great deal of experience at failure, it does not surprise me that hundreds of people can "look" at a Facebook post and less than 10 have the "generosity to "like" it and the likelihood of one of them sharing it is virtually non-existent. I know it must be quite a risk to actually "share" something that another has done as I note that there are many occasions when a poster challenges those who are giving their post a "look" to give it a "share". They usually read something like, "Those in uniform deserve my respect. I'll bet most people won't have the guts to share this."

Much of the time this is a repost from what seems like a "bot". I can hardly imagine anyone but a social media sociopath actually demanding an agreement on something that is contentious, claiming that it is lack of courage that dictates one's choice, while the hordes that haunt social media apparently don't have the "guts" to even post a like on something that is a neutral human experience. Folks claim they are being selective when they don't "like" a piece of artwork and would think it quite ridiculous to be challenged to "like" something merely because a friend or acquaintance has posted it. At the end of the day, social media has exposed much of humankind as being jealous, envious, show-offs whose psychotic adherence to a zero-sum mentality won't allow them to be human or kind. Most monetize their own preferences, "likes", which means they give only to those who they feel worthy, those who already have the fame and fortune they seek, while ignoring and berating those who seek a nod of approval for any sort of creative achievement.

Begpacking has become an industry*. Those who do it in the streets are only a physical reminder of this. A failed artist is perhaps the worst. He begs a reality that mocks the virtual world. A true artist is one who creates without creating. He who mimics reality most closely has the most talent. If one can create something abstract using a method which robs the work of most of the human element, a bucket full of holes swinging on a rope, a bit of paint splashed on a spinning canvas, one can be a genius. If one is so absurd as to toil behind a tool in one's hand with only one's soul for direction, this one is a fool.

Manual labour is for the weak of mind, the impoverished soul. True achievement comes through efficiency. Efficiency comes from investment in stocks and bonds and the labour of others, pyramid schemes the norm, even those who labour seek escape in this form. Life is a template, a triangular tower which must be scaled if one is to succeed. Those whose attempts to create are not to fulfil a material need, should kneel to those who are guided by greed. Begpackers are merely an extension of a world of full of mendicants whose goal is to live by luck and the good fortune of others, a universe where an investment in an artificial economic entity, a stock market or a lottery, brings greater reward than an investment in one's self and God forbid one's creativity.

*Call it advertising, updating, or whatever you may but to me it is just a bunch of online mendicants sticking their hands out and sometimes putting them in my pocket. There is a violation of spirit, an emotional rape that one incurs when one is constantly confronted with a pitch for sales. It is no different than one is followed by a physical person hounding them for spare change or an exact amount which they say they are seeking for a physical need. The conscience swirls despite one's best attempt at defying the temptation of compassion. Empathy dies as the user watches three seconds after three seconds and flashes of skip ad that attempt to guilt one into compliance, a kind of "buyance" where one agrees to buy not because he or she wants or needs the thing but rather feels like they are cheating someone out of their just deserts.

The First Drop

No matter where I am, I always catch the first drop of rain. Whether it is a sun shower or a deluge, there is always a bit of doubt or perhaps hope from those around me. It looks like rain I will say. No. The rain won't come for some time. They will say or something to that effect. It is raining I will say. I just caught the first drop. The hope or doubt will continue; then they will feel a drop. Wow. It's raining they will say as though it is an epiphany, an invention of their own. I recognize my own insignificance as I realize that my drop had been completely ignored. I wonder then if there is such a thing as a god, a higher power. The drop is sent to me so that I know I truly have a purpose, something to live for, even if that purpose is to be ignored.

Absolution

As a failed artist, I often feel alone. I am sure that this feeling is shared by most if not all and I gain confidence with this feeling. It is sad that we are the most alone with our failure. Though it is said that misery loves company, true misery loves solitude. Whiners love company. And while they may be miserable and love company, they do not love misery. Misery is for the lonely and alone.

One learns through experience that one is most alone when he/she is in the company of loved ones but feels unloved. The "black sheep" that fails to fit in, not for failure to fit in but rather for nothing to fit in to. The "prodigal son/daughter" who returns to the open arms of those whose minds and hearts have closed.

Is it true that most of us spend much of our life making up for lost time, making up for mistakes that cannot be corrected, sins that will not be absolved? Is there an epiphany when the dust has settled on the dead horse we daily beat? Stirring it up only dulls one's vision. One can only live in a present which is ephemeral and fleeting. Hurtful words that one spews can't be taken back and souls can't be mended. The scars that one creates are not healed by one's philanthropy and even the kindest words can sometimes create scars. Especially when doled out like presents; they become gifts of condescension.

The judgemental tend to believe they are forces of nature that hold the universe intact just as those with wealth believe they have created that which they hoard, disregarding that even the most creative inventions require an army of people to produce, sell and consume them. The failure to understand that they are less than a wisp of wind to the sands of time that swirl about us scarcely impeded by the whims of humans is true failure.

My failure to maintain anger and grudge has often made me a target for both. There is nothing that makes one seem more arrogant than the lack of jealousy and envy that one is supposed to sustain when dealing with those who intend to provoke such feelings whether through wealth of material or social position.

I find compliments are like so many coins that one doles out. When given generously, they are pocketed and kept, becoming slaves of those who receive them. When given sparingly, the become tools of the devil. They swirl about in the mind like a current of doubt.

The art exhibition was somewhat of a success. The food and drink were plentiful and Van, the owner of the venue, became more pleasant and pleased as the night went on. I snuck in a couple of bites as I had forsaken lunch and dinner in setting up for the show. He saw me and he chuckled and told me that I shouldn't be eating so much so quickly as he was going live on his social media feed. I mentioned that he didn't need to film that which he found distasteful. His chuckle became a full-bodied laugh as he is one who is fond of cutting mockery when it is he who is wielding the sword.

I kept my temper intact despite the desire to shove his phone down his throat, and I smiled and laughed with him. I mentioned that I was drinking from the expensive bottle of wine which I had bought from him.

The complimentary food and beverages that were to be taken by guests were originally at the rear of gallery restaurant so that invitees would amble through the place and check out the artwork as they did. As the night went on, I was impressed by his generosity but a bit troubled by the fact that his servers were now scrambling about taking food to tables making it difficult for the guests to move about and it seemed his intention to change the focus of the evening. I was still pleased at the attendance, and I made my way around the tables encouraging guests to "have a look", emphasizing that all the works were for sale.

I recognize that most attendees at virtually any event are there primarily for the "Bling "the free stuff that they receive and can brag about on social media or by displaying it in their "cribs". I heard that they are called "balloon chasers" by a Swiss friend of mine, He owns an upscale Swiss restaurant in Bangkok and at one of his events I noted that he was serving the folks at my table food and wine that was on an entirely different level than those around us. I felt a bit guilty, but he explained. "It is because you are customers." he explained in his matter-of-fact Swiss accent. "Those others are balloon chasers. They only come in when things are free."

I tried not to interrupt the "customers" as the wait staff bulled around me as though I was a pylon on an obstacle course. I noted the other two artists were more inclined to recline in their respective thrones, apparently confident that their art would "sell itself" or that they were well enough known that having a physical presence was not so necessary. I have often noted at shared events that, in the zero-sum game that has become life, my fellow artists rarely mingle except for periodic celebrity appearances whenever they think I am going to sell a piece of my work and then they appear by my side as though they had been standing next to me throughout the night. And their appearance is not to draw attention towards them but rather away from me. My gain would be their loss so they will have an urgent matter to discuss about something that is entirely irrelevant but needs to be resolved immediately. And this is what goes for collaboration among the free spirits of the art world!

Is Networking dead?

It is not important to me to be an artist. It is important to me to make art.

In order to be a true failure in the art world, one must give up the idea of being a successful artist. For one to be a failed artist one must give up that which identifies one as being an artist.

This may seem odd or contradictory, but I have learned that anytime I am being an "artist", I am failing to be that which I consider most to being an artist. Art, you should see, is something that people can immediately relate to, whether their relationship with art is the dismissal of it or a claimed kinship, it is a rare individual who does not hold a firm opinion as to what art should and should not be.

An artist should be the opposite, whether one knows him/her or not, the artist must be a puzzle, someone with whom others have an immediate understanding while having no understanding at all. An artist must be someone who strives to live on an edge that others will not peril, while not striving at all. It is not about tilted berets and well-tied scarves. Her or his work must make a statement yet not be contrived. The statement must be understood by those who truly appreciate the work that goes into the art. Art is not about talent or skill but rather work, a day-to-day struggle to produce something magical from the most mundane.

Art lovers must be those whose appreciation comes from education. Art education must come at the expense of taste and trial, it must inform the educated as to their role as aficionados of art. They must be discriminating in their tastes. This makes them consume art like caviar or vintage wines. They may not love the taste, but they love what it represents. It represents the finer things in life; that which others cannot afford to appreciate.

"Risking the Abstract" was the title of the exhibit. I chuckled as I read this, but it gave me an air of confidence when I decided to attend. I remember thinking "Great!" with a realization that abstract art might become mainstream here in Vietnam.

I suppose, if I was a real artist this would have been a body blow, something which struck me with a fear that I might become mainstream. And, if I, the great Ron, who is so audacious as to use his own name on his gallery, would become mainstream, who then would be Ron. Would Ron Art become a kind of Costco or Walmart for art? Would people be seeking reproductions and buying random works merely because they were abstract, and folks were willing to risk that abstract? Would painting become so two dimensional that texture and form would be lost in the charge to create images that were nothing more than caustic colours which shouted out to onlookers like the logos for brands such as Nike or Levi's? Would they then morph into a world where brands became more important than the product? Would the risky abstract replace realism, impressionism, and even surrealism as social media has replaced true friends with those from cyberspace?

I was pondering this as I prepared for the journey to the old film theatre where the exhibition was to be presented. I think this is what is defined as overthinking in this day and age. Any time one puts thought into something, it is considered overthinking. We have been taught through the plethora of advertising campaigns that we should just do it! (Of course, the contrarians out there, our close friends from the comments section, will throw out ideas about other campaigns which might provoke thought but…I lack their expertise in such matters and hereby declare to doom humanity to my opinion.) And to be truthful there is a lot to be said for just doing it. I am sure that I have achieved more, meaning completed, in my life by just doing it rather than actually having a goal which becomes a plan which becomes a series of goals which become a series of plans which become a series of unfulfilled goals.

My plans usually result in steps which need to be taken in a kind of order and this usually results in chaotic leaps from one plan to another and then a chase back to a part of the plan that needed to be completed before taking a next step.

Life without a plan has taken me to a degree at a university, a life which some seem to envy and a degree of freedom that seems scary to others and even to me from time to time. And this is a recipe for failure, and in that, I have had much success.

So, I did not choose my clothes carefully, I rarely do, but I did manage a jacket and a t-shirt which allows me to display prominently on my chest a painting which would be iconic were I a successful artist along with my own "Just Do It" though the letters on mine spell out "If you are not moving forward, you are in your way." Ron in my logo is given credit for this expression though it is uncommon that anyone who reads my shirt to me mentions this. I suppose I designed it like this to diminish my role as the author and to avoid the rare occurrence when one asks me to explain its origins much like those fond of mocking my creations which I like to overthink of as art.

I took a taxi, which I usually do when I am uncertain of a location, and I arrived near the venue but was still uncertain as to its location as it was not on the street. One needed to navigate one's way down a series of serpentine alleys. Fortunately, I had not arrived at the advertised time as I was offered guidance from a man who was and was now on his way out.

There were markers along the way, hip artsy folks, young and old munching away at the street food in the tiny stalls that lined the narrow alleys. Apparently, the free food and drink was yet to flow I overthought in the cynical way that I do. Were it not for the many moochers who seek the complimentary free for them food and drink, the art world might be all but dead.

I arrived there to find this to be true. The organizers had yet to begin serving and the staff was arranging bottles of Jim Beam, Gordon's and some other brands that I hadn't known were so common here in Hanoi. These were supplemented with the usual cheap wines and beers that are nearly always served at room temperature, here that means 80 F plus, so they are even more challenging to stomach by my fellow alcoholics.

As the nuts and chips were rationed onto the tiny child sized plates that were then placed out to feed the starving guests, the rush began. And typically, the prayer to the arts that must feed the soul just as the free for them food frees them from hunger began with the required fanfare which rarely stops the munching but does shut folks up.

As venues must be hip and hip must be confounding, the speakers crackled away spewing more crackle than verbiage which I am sure was just fine for the crowd. The humility of the artists was in its last stage, that stage where they oblige the art world with their homage to their humble beginnings as they humbly bow out to their introductions. They were all rags to riches stories. The reality that their wealthy families paid their way through art school knowing full well that their artist child would someday come to his or her senses and find their way into worthy employment was all but lost. Their valiant struggle against the tides of cash with which their family burdened them and were still fighting the good fight as they risked the abstract was unveiled!

One must recognize that it is easy and meaningless for a poor or middle-class person to become an artist. What is the risk in that? Poor is poor! But when those in the wealthy class forsake their family's wealth, well not really their wealth but the facades that they might have to maintain to appear as though they deserve it, that is real risk! Imagine! Having no security blanket except for the rich family members who obligatorily keep the artist in the six-figure income range by making their scheduled purchases whenever the artist needs to be invited to a show or to "earn" an endowment.

When the ceremony finished it was on to the next stage! The moochers largely left the tables barren which freed them to make their obligatory paces around the place, empty cups in hand like so many mendicants near a tourist attraction seeking out donations to their cause. The servers had become stingy with the drink as the real invitees, the VIPs, who have the good sense to avoid the ceremonies, began to appear and the curators rushed around greeting them. I noted that the bourbon had changed brands, and I went to secure a sip of the nectar of those particular gods.

Grudgingly I was given a cup but only after a young attractive lady, wearing the spandex pants that seem a required rite of passage here and sporting a pink streak in her hair, a member of the all-important local press, identified me as a near VIP by asking me if I was "that artist" while I was ordering the drink. Of course I was, I assured her, cementing her place in those in the know, how dare those who were not???

She followed me around breathing into my face, her breath smelling of cock, and I wondered if I would be risking the abstract if I asked her to suck mine. She was literally drooling. I wondered if her open mouth's constant presence near my nose was meant to be a great enough hint so that I wouldn't have to ask. I saw her gazing at one of the featured artists while she tied back her shiny black and pink hair. I wondered if her halitosis had its origin in the sweaty depths of his crotch.

I noticed she had abandoned me. Though she was still physically standing next to me, she was no longer present. Admittedly I am not one so good at taking hints and I was confident she would find someone else to do as there were plenty of folks who outranked me there in the order of importance in the "art world". I approached one of the featured artists, whose claim to fame was fame, he was so famous that his work had shown in New York and Paris, as well as other important parts.

Despite his travels, his communication skills seemed rather weak. I was surprised that a man so travelled would have such little grasp of English. I tried French but failed in that as well. I guessed that he probably had a good command of both but was not about to break ice with yet another foreign pretender who lived in Vietnam but was unable to communicate in Vietnamese. Like a country bumpkin in the states or a bogan in Australia who insists that visitors "talk English" many here think speaking the local language has something to do with respect rather than the difficulty of the language and the absolutely horrible teaching methods here. He had lost touch with his humility and had become the asshole that we all are when we feel our territory being encroached or that one fails to recognize our importance, I knew then that it wasn't a language issue.

Though his behaviour was stand offish, he seemed to be regressing back to the shy humble fellow who earlier had ducked his head into his chest as the audience applauded his introduction. I humbly took my leave recognising the futility of this interaction. I understand that, as artists, we are obliged to stand in front of a piece of work and wax eloquent, whether in word or gesture. Jaws agape, we must have a sort of meeting of souls regardless of any linguistic exchange. And far be it from me to claim "artist" among such giants. Though I truly love art, especially when it is displayed publicly whether in the wonderfully curated confines of museums and galleries or in the freedom of the streets, I rarely have time for the pretence that goes with it.

As I took my leave, I saw the journalist cozying up to a tall young American man who was yet another accomplished artist. They were standing under a kind of spotlight and the sheen off his balding head was nearly blinding. I was tempted to stand under it with my own bald head and give him a good dose of his own medicine. He seemed quite full of himself, getting the journalist's attention. The woman next to him, most likely his wife, was giving him a "get the hell away from her" tug every 30 seconds or so. I confess that I should have looked away. Sadly, I often find my eyes wandering from the other arts when there is a bit of human drama to behold and there always is at such events. I am sure that this lack of focus contributes greatly to making my failure as an artist complete.

Oh... Did I forget to mention that the curator who was running the show managed to dodge a simple goodbye just as she had dodged the flowers and wine I had presented her earlier. I wish I could state that this was because I was hopelessly drunk, but I was on my best behaviour. When I had once visited her at her gallery, she had made the mistake of complimenting me and I made the mistake of accepting the compliment. I have come to wonder if there is such a thing as a pure compliment. I am no longer young, but age comes to everyone. What should have come off as an advance, a proposition of intimacy, was interpreted as a true appreciation of my work. Maybe it was. Whatever it was, it did not rate me as an occupant of her circle. A friend of hers blocked me from my path once again. This time, empty handed, I accepted my prize, anonymity. There is nothing quite like it for a failed artist.

Messianic is a word that comes to mind. Though I believe most of us bow to the dollar gods, there are others. Cool has become one of those gods. Perhaps it always was important but being cool is nearly as important as being rich, though being rich buys lots of cool. It is quite rare however, to meet someone who is actually cool. How do I define cool? Maybe free from care? Not counting down to the very last digit when a check comes. As gracious in buying rounds as when one is bought for them. One who actually minds his or her own business but can still be counted on for support. But wait... I wrote messianic. This has nothing to do with cool.

I thought I was tucked away safely as I busied myself typing at the café near my house. I live in a small village, and it is a shock that such a trendy space exists here. A local guy entered. He was very slight but wore clothes that would have fit someone twice his size.

It seemed he was shocked and maybe a bit appalled to see a foreigner. He stared at me, and I kept typing away, intentionally ignoring him. He walked over to a table near mine. He was staring directly at me but ducked his head when I looked back at him. As he approached, he feigned a trip and then gave a cord on the floor a kick. It seemed he thought it was connected to me. He looked apologetic, not to me but to himself realizing that the cord was not connected to me. As the fan to which it was connected spun its last spins, I guessed that he thought it would shut me down. I wondered if he had ever used a computer or heard of a battery. I laughed so hard that he couldn't do anything other than join me. Not in a coffee mind you, just in the laugh. He gave me one last mean mug as he sauntered out of the place, shoulders back and chest puffed out like a weightlifter. His clothes nearly fit in his puffed-up state...

Je Suis en Retard... again

I arrived late. The patron was already there, and he was waiting on the first floor rather than ascending to the second-floor exhibition. I have seen him happier. I know not why but I have been late to appointments with him more often than not. And this does not find its foundation in carelessness or lack of respect but just really bad luck. The gallery in which we were meeting was located on a small street which shared its name with a much bigger street about 30 minutes away in another section of Hanoi. Google maps being what it is, directed me to the identical address on the other side of town. When I explained this the patron viewed the inviter with a bit of suspicion, as he was a competing artist. He said, incredulously, "If you would have given me the address; that is where I would have gone." He then directed his contempt at the host of the exhibition, a competing artist, and asked him why he didn't just tell me it was in Tay Ho. I had never noticed that the artist had a stutter, but it became apparent as it was an obvious attempt at misdirection. Such is collaboration in the art world.

The patron was a bit relieved that I had actually made an attempt at being prompt. He had grown tired of my tardiness. His office is in one of the most difficult spots in Hanoi. In addition to the ever-present traffic in the area, there are constant detours due to the construction of the project with no end, also known as the sky train, and it doesn't matter from which side of the city one makes an approach, driving a car to his place is a genuine hardship. It is not good sense that has others on time when we have scheduled a meeting with more than the two of us, it is that they cannot or will not afford a car. Several of the streets leading to his office, which I call his orifice, are one way for cars but not motorbikes. This makes it even more difficult for cars as motorbikes can be very wide and it only takes two of them, one in each lane, to cause one of the jams that often seem as inexplicable as they are numerous. I have seen two motorbikes race down a one way for cars street and suddenly, as though in formation, simultaneously take U-turns without either of them completing their U. This results in an immediate jam and an argument that apparently looks to escalate to one of the street fights that folks seem to find so entertaining, so they are less likely to honk their horns to clear the duelling duo from the street than they are to take out their phones to film them.

On one occasion, a saboteur collaborated in a tardy. I had not known prior to arriving at her workplace to pick her up that she had her own agenda. It was my understanding that she was only going to interpret but I should have known. I have yet to have an interpreter come to a meeting to interpret. They come to meet other foreigners and rich locals, and to present themselves as worthy company. I should have suggested she take a cab, but she insisted that she would be "right on time". And she was.

By the time she got out of the important emergency meeting that was spontaneously called by her, she is some sort of manager in a bank, it was time to start that meeting that was at least 45 minutes away. As I grinded my way through the distracted and directionless five o'clock madness, I wished that I had anti-grinding teeth guard that I sleep with for moments like this that haunt me in the night.

She busied herself sending important messages to her children who are apparently helpless but mostly fought to achieve a new level on one of the many games that busy people like her play on their phones. I began to suspect that this is what the emergency had been. My temper was rising as was the temperature in car. Being surrounded by fellow fuel burners can rarely be described as a pleasure and is probably the leading cause of deaths due to stress in any populated zone.

"Where do we turn?" I asked.

She continued to play.

"Are you going to tell me when I need to turn?" I asked.

I knew what she wanted. She wanted a tantrum. You see, foreigners are famous for losing their temper while the locals NEVER do. And of course, locals are kind to foreigners and would certainly never do anything to upset them!

"Could you grow up and put your phone away?" I said too loudly for the little space in the car.

"I have to make sure my kids are ok!" she protested.

"Oh! Are they in the game?" I said calmly.

"I am not playing a game!" she lied. "I am just waiting for them to reply."

I don't think her fingers stopped moving even after I convinced her that I really did need directions.

"But you have been there before!" she exclaimed!

"Yes. I was taken there several times. But I have never driven there myself. It's different you know?"

It was then that she began to espouse her sermon. She wanted Mr. Lee to hire her, and she was going to ask him to pay her what she was worth! I knew that she had worked for him before, but this was the first I had heard of this deal. Apparently, she had intended on being late as this is something that she knows makes him angry and was probably the reason they ended up parting ways in the first place. She was interested in my project, connecting artists with his architectural firm to provide artworks for buildings he designs. It could be a "win win" all the way around but she was going to make certain that she was going to receive a salary which I could not agree to as it was to be paid by Mr. Lee but that I was supposed to agree to propose as I had included a kind of liaison officer who is bilingual in my proposal.

I was almost certain that Mr. Lee would not agree to this, and I began to suspect that the two had had one of those untenable affairs where it is either compensation or commitment and it is not a "win win" for either.

She lucked into a phone call which then led to a series of messages, and I knew we were very close to the hidden entrance to the alleyway that led to his office building because she was ignoring me as she pressed her face into her phone screen. It was her final act of defiance to his beloved time schedule as she steeled herself for the confrontation that I could not have predicted I was set to endure.

The meeting was predictable though. I kept my phrases slow and short while her translations were quick and long. I felt like the entire purpose of the meeting was to piss off Mr. Lee and to assure the other artists and guest that I was an inconsiderate asshole who cared nothing for them or their time. I would learn later that one of them had accused "us", the interpreter and I had apparently come as a team, of just trying to make money of off "them". I assured "them", according to her, that both of "us" had well-paying jobs and we didn't need anything from them.

"Why did you answer that?" I said more amused than upset.

"Well, they can't talk to us like that!" she replied with pride.

"But weren't you supposed to be translating?"

"Well, I was! And if we are going to work together, you are going to have to get used to that."

If there a meter to measure her self-satisfaction at that moment, I am sure it would have hit a maximum value. I remember wondering why I even try. "Try failing next time." I thought she must be thinking. "Failure looks good on you."

Finding poverty among the wealthy

The Wealth of my poverty

I was walking around combing the gutters for cigarette butts; amazing what people toss away. I had no cash to buy my own pack so I was compiling a pack from the barely smoked butts that I would find. It wasn't my first recycling operation. I was learned. I knew where to go to get the best butts.

I was living in Nice, living the good life. The beauty of the place kind of erased any of the bad feelings I had about being broke. I was staying in a very nice place provided by the friend of a friend. They did not know that I could not make the rent.

It was located near several of the upscale clubs where people would stand in line for hours to get in. I would join them in line sometimes just to have something to do.

I noted that folks would often light cigarettes and then almost immediately put them out and toss them away if the line so much as twitched. I think smoking inside might have been allowed, but I did note that the doormen had folks put out their smokes before going inside. The shiny brass ashtray to the left of the gaudy gold painted entrance looked like a treasure trove as the folks stuffed their cigarettes into the sand.

When I got near the front, I would mumble some excuse and head to the back of the line or head back to my apartment to get my wallet. At least that was the excuse I would mumble. I would always find a couple of good butts on the walk home as I schemed away. Fortunately, the prior residents of the apartment had left a fair

217

collection of alcohol, mostly aperitifs, so I could have a drink and a smoke.

I ran a good bit and exercised regularly. I suppose that explained my gaunt appearance as much as the wrestlers' diet that I maintained. I had met a girl on the beach, a tiny spoiled rich Thai girl who spoke English fluently. She said her dad was English, but he was not her father. She was a bit chunky and a lot insecure. The beautiful bronze of her skin was interrupted in places by the white scar tissue of stretch marks. As a kind of apology for her girth, she told me that she decided to maintain her weight as dieting depressed her. This seemed quite sad to me as she looked more athletic than fat and probably weighed a grand total of fifty kilos.

She liked to bring groceries to my house. She did not cook though she claimed to have learned. She had an English name, Sarah. She would not share her Thai name and I did not insist.

She had no problem getting dates. She told me this. Frenchmen love exotic women and her body screamed sexuality and her smile submissiveness. She then informed that she had a hard time keeping a boyfriend.

Sarah had a kind of hobby. She would meet guys at the beach or on the street. Nice is a good place for that. She would go to dinner with them, often at a fairly upscale place, and then without eating what she ordered, she would insist they take her home. They all agreed enthusiastically as they thought this would lead to sex. She would then ask for a take home container. They would take her to my place, and we would enjoy this along with her story about the guy's behaviour.

More often than not, there would be a shouting match when they would arrive at the building as her date would insist on going up to her apartment and she would insist that they didn't.

Sarah would tell them that her roommate, a female, would be very upset and did not allow visitors. She advised me rather firmly not to intervene, I suppose it was good advice, and I did not though it was clear that some of her suitors were a bit rough with her. I guessed she didn't mind this as she did not complain and I suppose that she did understand that I would have come to her aid anonymously, like I was just another resident of the building, if things got too serious.

This went on for a few weeks. It was not fun for me as I always empathised with the guy she was scamming regardless of what she would say. And she would nearly drag me to the bed and absolutely attack as though she was on a sort of aphrodisiac. She began to tell stories about how French guys treated her and she seemed obsessed with sex. It was a bit shocking to me that she was basically just trolling for men and her whole existence revolved around sex. It was as though she was a kind of sex slave who had no choice in the matter. All of our conversations led to sex and any time we were not having sex seemed like wasted time to her.

Unfortunately for us, I found myself, almost unable to perform. There was something so distasteful about her conversation that I just couldn't come to terms with our relationship, and it was affecting me physically. I was more than a bit surprised by this as I was in excellent physical condition and our first couple of encounters lasted entire evenings, continued on in mostly sleepless nights and ended with a drawn-out session in the morning.

As my performance waned, she began to complain, all the while going into minute detail about acts which I sometimes thought better mentioned to the police. She was a victim in her stories. It was as though she was being kidnapped over and over and kept as a helpless slave to the desires of the men who were imprisoning her. I have always been a sucker for a sad story, but her tales were surreal. Her second-hand generosity began to seem more an act of revenge against those who would make her their victim than any concern for my well-being.

After one uneventful night, she quit coming. I am sure that her insecurity got the better of her and she decided that she was no longer attractive to me physically. This might have been the case though I know it was her constant banter that turned me off completely. I suppose we must have but I don't recall ever communicating by telephone. I had no way of contacting her and even less desire.

About a week later, I saw her at Place Massena with a very handsome young Frenchman. They looked good together. He smiled at me. He must have known something I didn't, and she looked a bit like she was pouting, perhaps about to cry. I recalled our first nights together when I would paint her body without paint on my brush, stroking her into a state where she seemed almost unconscious. The look on her face was familiar. I could not look away. I wondered if that was what she was feeling as the cool evening breeze lifted her dress to expose her plump brown thighs. It was as though she was a painting that needed finishing.

I stepped on something soft and when I looked down, I saw what I thought was an empty pack of cigarettes. They had been discarded or perhaps dropped. They must have been dropped because there were three left in the pack. I looked around to see if anyone was looking for them. When I looked back in her direction, they had disappeared. The space that they had occupied was now empty; like a place on a canvas that yearned for the loving strokes of a brush. I felt the need to paint but more the desire to smoke. When I returned to the apartment to have a drink with my smoke, I saw a portrait of her that I had quick sketched with my pencil on a notepad. She was magnificent. As I poured my second ouzo into a crystal champagne cup, I wondered how I had failed to notice that.

A Bestie

I don't like people much, despite my best efforts. I am judgemental which makes interactions with folks almost entirely regrettable. Friends become foes and foes friends of convenience; disappointment is always lurking in the dark corners of my mind. It is rare and almost inevitable that I find fault where there is none and I live in a constant battle with a desire to be social without any sort of desire to find friendship. I find the desire to mock to be the most prevalent goal of almost all of the people with whom I relate, it seems one can find envy in virtually anything. Solitude when one is alone is not solitude. One must seek out a crowd to exercise one's anonymity. Solitude among a mass of people is where one is truly alone.

I rarely make contentious comments on social media. When I read remarks from the advocates of the devil which pervade social media, I sometimes wonder how awful the person's life must be. To find pleasure in airing out one's grief to the groups of strangers that haunt the internet seems foul. As I say, I am judgemental.

I was shocked to see that a "friend" of mine, I guess I should judge him more an acquaintance, made certain to compose a nasty comment about anything that I posted that was art related. I shouldn't have been surprised as he made similar comments to my face. My surprise came from the fact that I was constantly defending him, as the owner of a restaurant, in that same forum. Personal issues had been destroying him and he took anything even remotely negative that was posted about his restaurant personally.

I recall when I began to truly note his disdain for me, of which my art was merely a minor element, a kind of blasting off point for his contempt.

A lady friend of mine named Thuy mentioned that we should go see Tom, the friend, after we had a triumphant day at an upscale local market where we were offering my paintings for sale.

"Tom will be so happy for you!" She cooed, "You really need to share this with him."

I had not suspected that they were having relations as he was a married man. He played the role of a devoted father though I never witnessed him displaying any warmth towards his wife so I could have guessed their relationship was more of convenience than love as I assume most to be.

We arrived at his place, and he ducked down into his computer. In retrospect, I suppose he had already been warned. I doubt that Thuy could have resisted sending him a message that would have crushed his soul, I have judged that technology speeds the rate of all, especially delivering vendetta and malice. I should add that I live in a world dominated by deception and deceit where moments lacking this are nearly too rare to note.

We ordered a couple of glasses of champagne and a non-alcoholic drink for Thuy. Tom shrugged this off as he busied himself on his laptop as he often did when he did not have a drink in his hand. He resisted my drink, and barely acknowledged our presence. In retrospect, I am sure he had been warned. I felt more than a bit lonely as Thuy became playfully insistent on sharing the motive of our visit.

Thuy laid out the cash, about 800 US dollars, and pushed it over to me as she smiled at him. I guess, for her, it was to entice him to place a higher value on her.

The cruelty of the situation was creeping in and felt it best to leave but Thuy resisted this and insisted that I ask Tom whether he was going to toast and if he wasn't, he should push the glass my way so at least I could enjoy it. This brought a bit of a grimace to his face though I judged it a smile and he enthusiastically slid the crystal champagne flute towards me.

He mumbled something and chuckled as he continued his "work". Thuy was the face of innocence as we clicked glasses, and I downed my champagne like it was a real toast. We left without saying goodbye and crawled back into the blazing black interior of my Chevy Spark. The smell of oil paint was thick. It made it even more difficult to breathe the hot, stale air in the car. "Well, you were certainly right about that!" I said sarcastically. "He could hardly contain himself."

I know that she resisted a laugh as the joke was on me and if she was to laugh, I might think it was my humour. The short ride to my house was filled with bliss for her; two men had just taken a drubbing and she was feeling the rush of victory. And I should have been as well. I have become so successful in my failures that even my victories are marred by defeat. I had achieved near perfection in this one.

Doubt

You see, or maybe you don't, I don't care about selling a painting unless it is for a life-changing amount of money or... I might sell one for nothing. But this does not mean I would be giving it away for free. I sell it for nothing but the interest one has for the work, not necessarily the painting but the work. The acquisition of the thought, the experience, the desire to put the thought to paint, to risk the fires of ignorance. For one who aspires to artistry, rather than mimicry, one must not only bear judgment of doubters, but will become one himself.

As accident erases intention and brush smooths over harsh scrapes of the pallet knives, raw talent gives way to practice as the eye of redundancy recalls that which it should see rather than that which it does. It calls to my mind that which a great martial artist said about winners and losers. "Winners think about winning. Losers think about winners." One must not allow doubt in oneself to creep into one's work, especially if that doubt comes from another. Even if that other were the greatest artist of all time, if such a beast were to exist. One's work is one's own, if it is not, one may might as well be a copying machine. I suppose it is advisable and clever to study the work of others but to focus on oneself on this is a selfish bow to vanity rather than a bow of respect. It is a focus on a winner. Only a loser would do this.

When the successful are criticized, they can afford to bark back. When a failure is criticized, he must take it as compliment, after all, it is the recognition that he is actually failing at something. If he is to reply to condescension, this means he is disabled... insecure.

All depends on one's degree of failure and one's ability to continue to fail against all odds. And failure like success can be fleeting. One must enjoy it while it lasts. The failure to understand this could leave one wallowing in it for the eternity that life sometimes seems. Fail big they say. Only the successful can play that tune. Fail small I say. Take it note by note. Failure is a pleasure that only a proud few can truly experience. Cherish the humanity of it. Live the insanity of it. Perish thoughts of success. Dignity only rises from the ashes of true failure.

Time for a recharge

"One of the things that I have come to understand is that artists are meant to be misunderstood. Even in this I find it hard to make folks understand. There is this perception that artists do very little other than create art in whatever medium they claim to be their speciality. And, for the non-artist this is helpful as they can immediately communicate their "understanding" with the artist.

Granted, many of the artists that I have met do very little more than casually put together pieces of work, usually spending at least an hour or two every day at their labours. They also spend time meeting with other artist friends and while away the hours of their day drinking tea and smoking cigarettes and those of the night drinking beer and local wine and smoking cigarettes. It seems there is society of artists and within this society there is a culture and within the culture there is a counterculture that is very rigid in its rules and expectations despite all attempts at pretending a kind of bohemian freedom.

It seems, for example, that any kind of physical labour is a bit beyond their realm. Simple things such as hanging work and cleaning up are beneath the artists despite humble words and their maintenance of a façade of humility. I have been amazed by denials of material wealth when the artists throw parties in their unusually spotless studios. They almost always serve local food that is a statement of the pledge to the poverty of an artist, almost like offerings at a temple. You see, one must always give the appearance of being poor but... poor cannot be messy or unorganized. In the same way that most of the abstract artists are abstract only in style, their lifestyles are only bohemian in their superficial behaviours. They must wear simple casual clothing, but it must all be expensive designer wear, or it would not be cool. They must ride simple motorbikes to and from their workshops but whenever they arrive at an event where they are in public eye, they must drunkenly spill out of a luxury ride, as though they are rock stars, yet when asked, most deny a privileged upbringing preferring stories of separations from wealthy parents who disagree with their pursuits of their passions. Yet... they hypocritically describe those same parents as hard-working entrepreneurial types whose creativity shot them to the top of their fields moments after mentioning that their grandparents were descendants of some sort of royalty to give themselves a boost in the DNA department."

I had been watching her smirk and squirm throughout my soliloquy. I knew that she would. I was talking about another artist that she was sleeping with. I had found out in a rather unfortunate way...but is there any way to find out such a thing which is fortunate?

The sound of the door opening and then slamming shut was sweet. The sweet sound of freedom. I heard the door open again but there was no slam. Some folks just don't know how to close the door behind them.

"You deserve to be alone!" she threatened.

"You are right I do! I deserve to be alone!!!!! I work hard enough at it. You are right. I need to get the hell away from you!!"

For once in my life, I had made a real decision, no doubt, no second guessing, I was gone. I felt the affirmation of this decision as I heard her chasing behind me. I knew that she could not catch me, and I did not even believe she was trying. Then my knee began to remind me that I can't actually run more than a few steps before what little cartilage that I have in my knee gives way.

"I can't live without you!" she yelled. I looked back to see her flip her shoulder length black hair up and smile.

I felt desperate. I knew that I wasn't going back this time. I had nothing left to lose. I was down to a couple of pairs of heavily worn shoes, two tailored suits, some holey underwear, a dozen or so mismatched socks and a bunch of paintings and art stuff that would be my sacrifices to the gods of good sense. I had been keeping my passport and wallet in the pocket of my old leather jacket. I grabbed it on my way out the door. I figured the clothes that I was wearing were sufficient for my new start and I was happy that I had the presence of soul to put on my 40-year-old Tony Lamas before I made the final decision to hit the road.

They have been through way too much with me to leave them behind. I knew that she knew I'd be back. Just as I knew that I wouldn't. It was an endless cycle that needed to be put to an end. One of the sadder things in life is that good habits are hard to maintain while bad habits are hard to break. But it is always best to break them so that they don't break you.